Tl
IRONSTONE
of tl
MIDLANDS

History, Operation and Railways

Part IX

Leicestershire

by

Eric Tonks
M.Sc.,F.R.I.C., Dip Maths.

Book Law Publications
Nottingham

ISBN 978-1-907094-09-5

First Published in 1992
by
Runpast Publishing

This Edition Published in 2009
by
Book Law Publications

Printed by The Amadeus Press, Cleckheaton, BD19 4TQ

Eastwell Quarries. A startling view from the overbridge, looking towards the top of the incline, with a row of full wagons ready to descend and two rows of empties waiting to be taken to the quarries. The haulage mechanism was in the building straddling the line at left.

K. Cooper/IRS Collection

Leicestershire

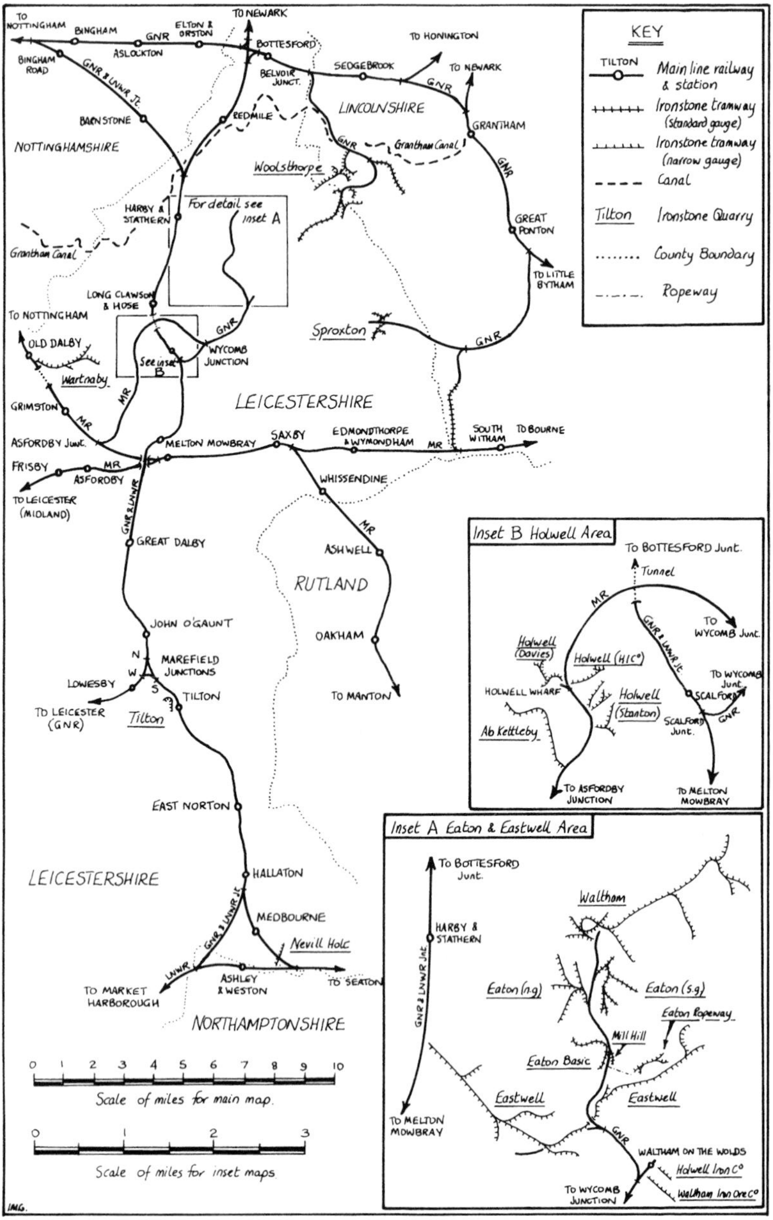

CONTENTS

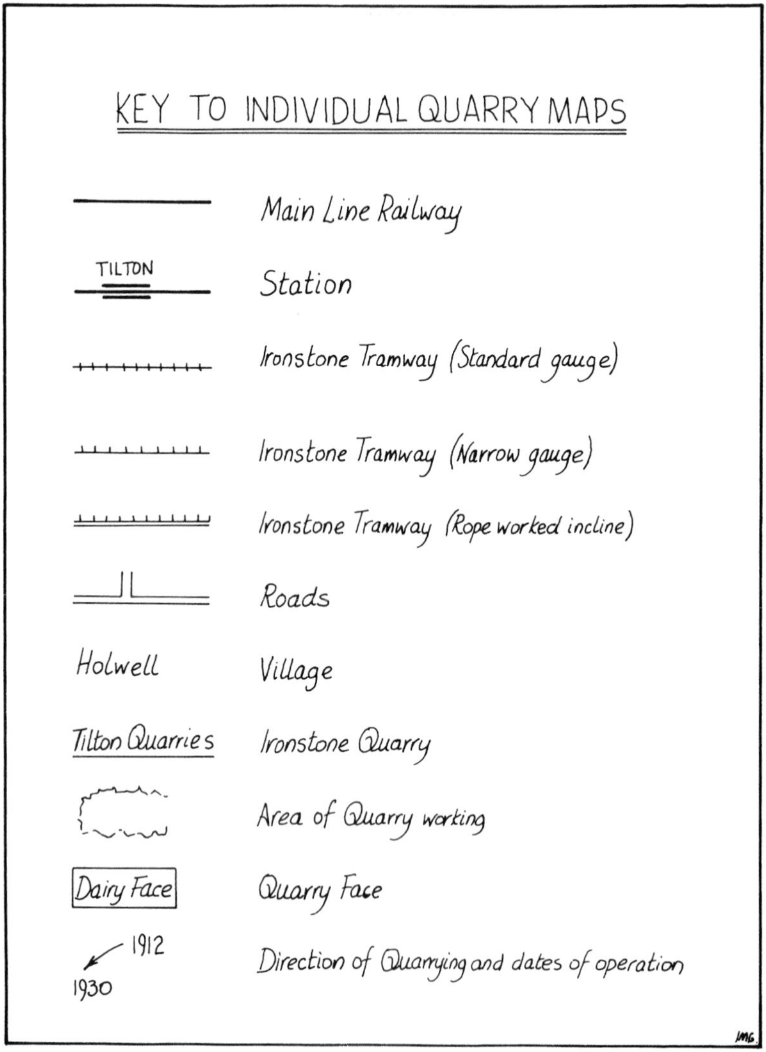
KEY TO INDIVIDUAL QUARRY MAPS
Main Line Railway
TILTON
Station
Ironstone Tramway (Standard gauge)
Ironstone Tramway (Narrow gauge)
Ironstone Tramway (Rope worked incline)
Roads
Holwell
Village
Tilton Quarries
Ironstone Quarry
Area of Quarry working
Dairy Face
Quarry Face
1912
1930
Direction of Quarrying and dates of operation
IMG.

INTRODUCTION

Leicestershire

With the exception of the isolated outcrops at Tilton and Nevill Holt, the ironstone of the Marlstone Rock in Leicestershire is confined to the outcrop between Melton Mowbray and Grantham, along the edge of the escarpment overlooking the Vale of Belvoir. There were a few quarries a little way back from the edge, in the Northampton Sand, but of these only Sproxton was of any consequence; Sproxton has indeed more affinities with the other quarries served by the High Dyke line, which were all in Lincolnshire. To the ironstone student Leicestershire is epitomised by the Marlstone quarries, a close-knit group of small systems, some of which lasted many years, calling for lengthy tramway extensions but retaining throughout the charm of the small rural railway. To the narrow gauge enthusiast they were a delight, set as they were in attractive countryside away from the main line railways and served almost entirely by mineral branches, themselves a pleasure to see in action. No wonder they received so much attention.

Development, as always, depended on the main line railways. The Marlstone Rock ironstone was discovered by J.A. Knipe in the course of preparing a geological map, and in his report he brought this important piece of information to the notice of the principal landowner, the Duke of Rutland, whose seat was at Belvoir Castle; but the distance from railways prohibited any economical development at the time. In 1855 the Clay Cross Co considered the possibility of working the Northampton Sand outcrop at Croxton Kerrial, but this too was abandoned for the same reason (see E. Wilson, 'The Lias Marlstone of Leicestershire as a source of Iron' in 'The Midland Naturalist', 1885, p61). Ironstone was then discovered at Holwell in the course of surveying for the Midland Railway line from Melton Mowbray to Nottingham, and development of the quarries in 1875 by the Holwell Iron Co anticipated the opening of the MR line by means of a three-mile connection that later became the MR Holwell branch. Events then moved rapidly; in 1879 Stanton Ironworks Co Ltd opened quarries both at Holwell and on the escarpment at Warnaby, the latter connected directly with the just-opened MR Nottingham line. Another new railway in the district was the GNR-LNWR Joint Line that traversed the Vale of Belvoir between Saxondale Junction and Melton Mowbray and at the nearest point to the Marlstone escarpment provided convenient access for quarries at Eastwell owned by Staveley Iron & Coal Co Ltd and their associates. Further south, cutting of this railway exposed a thick layer of ironstone at Tilton, which was worked by West Yorkshire Iron & Coal Co Ltd. Working at Eastwell and the quite isolated Tilton site commenced in 1881. Thereafter all quarries in Leicestershire were served by branches from the main line railways, notably the GNR branch to Waltham-on-the-Wolds (1882) and Eaton (1885) and their Denton branch (1885) serving the long-lived Woolsthorpe quarries. There were continuing developments at Holwell and Eaton up to the 1960s, some using lorry transport. Sproxton quarries, served by the LNER High Dyke line, were opened in 1925. Woolsthorpe and Harlaxton (Lincolnshire) were the last quarries 'North of the Welland' and their closure in 1974 brought to an end a hundred years of quarrying.

We are well supplied with information, in particular for the quarries owned by Stanton Ironworks Co Ltd, so excellently described in 'The Quarries' by H.B. Hewlett, published by Stanton in 1935 and fortunately still available to all by the Rutland Railway Museum reprint. Hewlett deals with all Stanton's quarries, starting off with the Leicestershire ones that one senses he found the most attractive. Stanton kept meticulous records too and these were preserved by their successors, Stewarts & Lloyds Minerals Ltd, at Sysonby Lodge, near Melton Mowbray; and it is to the people there in later years that we owe so much. They gave every encouragement and help to the amateur seeking information on any aspect of the ironstone industry, and the light mantle of their authority was reflected at the quarry offices, where similarly welcoming attitudes were general. The later files from Sysonby Lodge and the surveyor's plans, are available in BSC archives, including the Staveley group quarries that finally came into the S&LM field. Sproxton, the odd one out in Leicestershire quarries, is also well covered in the books donated to the Leicestershire Record Office.

Proportionately I have made more visits to Leicestershire than to other 'ironstone' counties, in the first place because of the special charm of their narrow gauge tramways and their setting in attractive countryside, and secondly because of the warmth of the welcome there; a visit to Belvoir became a social occasion, often including lunch with Tim Barclay and Bill Jones at 'The Chequers' at Woolsthorpe. Other visits were solitary, often ending with a late afternoon call at Eastwell locomotive shed to check the stock; in those days it was unusual to lock shed doors, and one could just lift the latch and see the five or six engines standing in a row, with a few of them 'sizzling' and all pervaded by the homely smell of steam and oil. There are regrets at lost opportunities of course – how I wish I had taken lots of photographs of the ropeway at Eaton, for example, and notes of the quarry machines. Tilton was remote from other ironstone quarries, and its history, fairly simple historically but exceedingly complex in terms of operating methods, was a study in itself, and for me it is always associated with George Ordish; he rarely went far and as Tilton was the nearest quarry to his home in Leicester, he knew it well. Similarly complex were the layouts at Holwell, the disentangling of which would have been impossible without the help of Page Hackett of long memory. And the history of working at Eaton, where the first straightforward rail operations were complicated by filling in by lorry operation. Jim Lees' help here was invaluable. But what fun it has all been!

I have given acknowledgement in the text to people who have contributed particular items of information. Special thanks are due to Ian Lloyd for his excellent maps, and to Martin Davies for his critical checking of the original draft, and help in copying archive photographs. I am very grateful to the many photographers who have kindly allowed me to use their work, and to the Rutland Railway Museum for allowing me to borrow items from their archives.

Birmingham 1992 Eric Tonks

For abbreviations used in the text and for terms used in the tables of locomotives and quarry machines, see 'Explanation of Tables'.

THE HOLWELL AREA

The ironstone industry of Leicestershire effectively began here, with a multiplicity of workings and tramways in a small area by a number of operators. With mining as well as quarrying involved, it has proved difficult to unravel their complex history, even with Hewlett's incomparable 'The Quarries' to guide us up to 1934 – and the latterday workings also posed problems (see 'Holwell Quarries' in the Industrial Railway Record, Vol 7, p 52). Fortunately, a good part of the Holwell site is now preserved in the interests of nature conservation, and these and other tangible remains help us to appreciate past events, as can also be said of the Wartnaby site a little further west; and it is lovely country to explore.

HOLWELL QUARRIES

Owners: Holwell Iron Co; Holwell Iron Co Ltd from 1880 (?)

These were the first commercially operated ironstone quarries in Leicestershire. Colonel Richard Dalgleish, a civil engineer employed by the Midland Railway and at that time engaged in carrying out a Parliamentary survey for their proposed line from Melton Mowbray to Nottingham, was struck by the redness of the soil in the Holwell district; he consulted his colleague Howard A. Allport of Barnsley, son of Sir James Allport, the General Manager of the Midland Railway, and in 1873 they examined the district by trial holes and sent samples of ore to Mr E. Riley of London for analysis[1]. With a favourable report from this, the partners then persuaded Sir James Allport to purchase a farm at Holwell to enable them to carry out further work. In 1874 samples were submitted to the Staveley Coal & Iron Co Ltd, who were impressed sufficiently favourably to commence negotiations with Allport for a lease of ground for quarrying; at first it seemed that Howard Allport would be prepared to lease both to them and to Stanton, but Allport and his colleagues then decided to work independently[2]. In 1875 Dalgleish left the railway service and went into partnership with Allport to form, in December 1875, the Holwell Iron Co, to lease the mineral rights on the farm and to sell the ironstone, with Dalgleish as managing director and Allport on the board. Within a few years both Stanton and Staveley had themselves leased ground in the district and the partners then decided to build their own ironworks on the spot[3]; the site chosen was the junction of the branch from Holwell with the Melton Mowbray-Nottingham line at Asfordby Hill but the works has always been known as Holwell Works from its association with the earlier quarrying activities. Foundations were laid in 1878 and the first furnace was tapped on 4th December 1881.

For the first few years ore was sold on the open market, commencing in 1875, according to Hewlett, and was at first presumably carted by road to the MR, whose line from Syston to Melton Mowbray had been in existence as far back a 1st September 1846: it was extended through to Peterborough on 1st May 1848; the Melton Mowbray-Nottingham line was later, being opened for freight traffic on 1st November 1879. However, temporary arrangements were made to accommodate the Holwell Iron Co's traffic before that date, as recorded in the minutes of the Nottingham & Melton Branch Committee of the MR, for extracts of which we are indebted to the Midland Railway historian John Gough and sent to us in January 1988 through our mutual friend Geoffrey Webb.

On 6th June 1876 this committee considered a letter of the preceding day from Howard Allport, and under Minute 99 resolved "That Mr. Underwood be requested to construct a temporary single line for about ¾of a mile from the Holwell Branch over the top of the hill at Asfordby Road to enable the Holwell Iron Co to take their ironstone into the Sidings adjoining the Syston and Peterboro' line at the Junction .." Minute 137 of the meeting on 6th February 1877 consists of an Engineer's Report of 31st January 1877 and relates "Holwell Branch is now being used but there is a difficulty in carrying on the traffic satisfactorily without some of the Permanent Way is laid from Melton Junction – 1 mile of Permanent Way materials laid in place would remove this difficulty, and would do away with any interference with the Contractors which is desirable". Since at the previous committee meeting of 2nd January 1877 there is no mention of traffic on the Holwell branch, it may be assumed that traffic began in January 1877.

E. Wilson (Loc.cit, p 62) confirms that the 3½ mile line from Holwell was laid by the quarry company in 1876, and this was worked by an 0-4-0ST supplied in 1876 as new by Hudswell Clarke & Rodgers but which was a rebuild of a Thornewill & Warham locomotive. E.M. Summers ('Holwell Works, 1875-1958' in 'The Stantonian' June 1958), states that the line to Asfordby was narrow gauge, but this appears to be erroneous.

The history of the standard gauge line has become confounded with the MR Holwell Branch on the same general alignment, but for a few years was indeed a pure ironstone system. The 6 ins OS (published in

1889 but surveyed in 1883/4) helps to confuse matters in depicting the line at Holwell in its original form but captioning it 'Midland Railway Holwell Branch'. The layout is confirmed by the Deposited Plans (dated November 1882) of the MR Holwell branch, which shows the layout existing before the MR took over. Particularly interesting is the line – evidently of standard gauge – from a trailing junction towards the quarries in the direction of 'The Willows' (see below), with a locomotive shed near the junction; while from a point about 200 yards east of the loco shed a 'tramway' is shown running dead straight for a quarter mile almost due north towards the four-road junction on the Six Hills road (Landyke Lane). Hewlett states that "the quarry roads had a gauge of three feet and the trams were hauled to the tipplers by horses"; the line shown on the November 1882 plan suggests a funicular, but it may not have been. End-tipping wagons can be presumed, possibly holding about 30cwt of ore. The 1883 OS shows the standard gauge line passing beneath the minor lane to Brown's Hill and crossing that to Scalford on the level in the direction of 'The Willows'; the survey maps indicate that the company exhausted pretty well all the available ore north of the lane as far as the Six Hills road and a short way south-east of the line as far as the Stanton lease. These areas were probably served by three foot feeders running to tipplers.

The junction of the standard gauge branch with the MR main line (Holwell Junction) is 250 feet above sea level, and, three miles north at a point close to the south-east of Holwell village, crosses the 400-foot contour and continues to climb; locomotives with trains of empties must have had to work hard. The ironstone outcrops around or just under the 500-foot contour, so the connecting tramways all had slopes with the load. At the terminus there seems to have been quite an extensive yard with sidings and a string of buildings called 'Holwell Huts', including a smithy and a brickyard. When the MR took over the standard gauge line as their Holwell branch, the layout at Holwell terminus was modified; instead of a standard gauge line making a trailing junction, there was a facing junction on the east side, either to the original or to a new tipping dock. No map showing this seems to have survived and the present-day pattern on the ground gives an incomplete picture. The Midland branch followed the same route as the original tramway, but put in a number of bridges where previously there had been level crossings; the best-known is that at the foot of the hill to the village, which included a small road diversion, and there is another one north of the latter-day tipping dock,

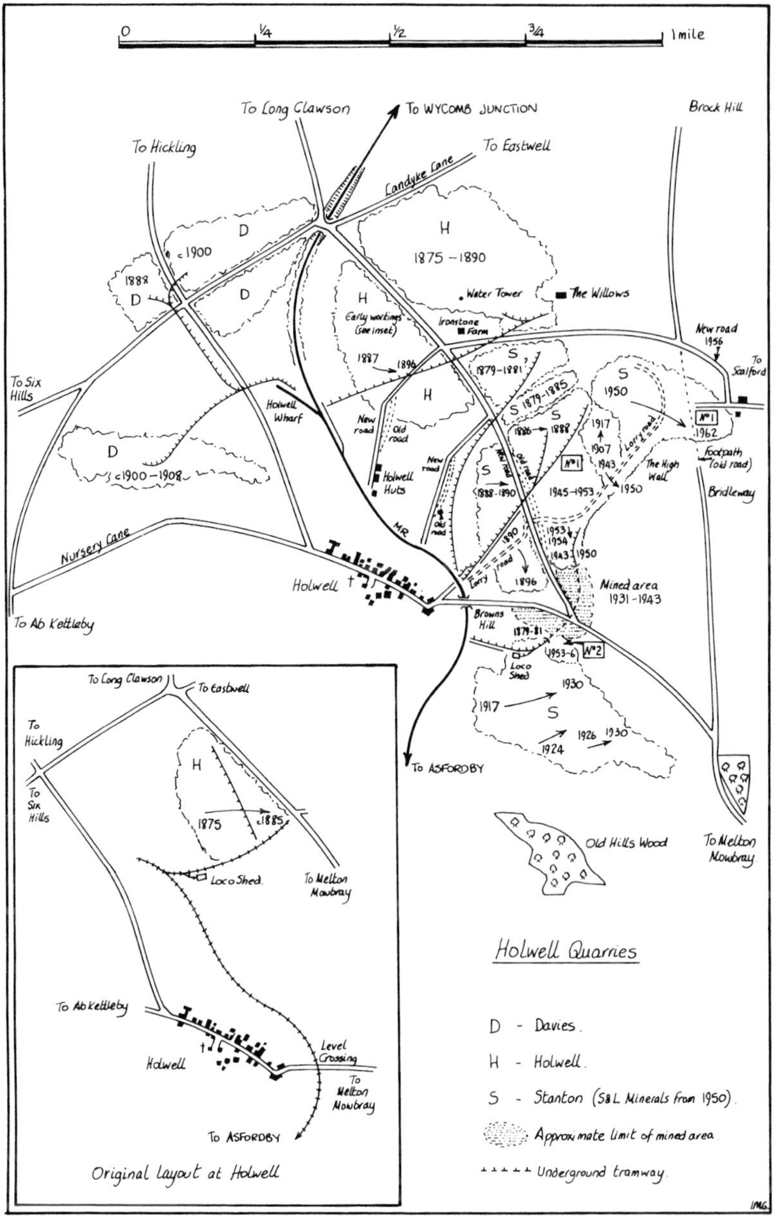

0
1/4
1/2
3/4
1 mile
To Long Clawson
To WYCOMB JUNCTION
Brock Hill
To Hickling
To Eastwell
Candyke Lane
D
H
1875 – 1890
c1900
1888
D
D
Water Tower
The Willows
H
Early workings (see inset)
Ironstone Farm
New road 1956
To Scalford
To Six Hills
1887
1896
S
1879–1881
S 1879–1885
S
1950
H
Holwell Wharf
New road
Old road
1886
1888
1917
1907
Lorry road
No1
1962
Footpath (old road)
D
c1900–1908
New road
S
1888-1890
No1
1943
The High Wall
1950
Bridleway
Holwell Huts
1945–1953
Nursery Lane
MR
Old road
1890
1953
1954
1943
1950
Lorry road
1896
Mined area 1931–1943
Holwell
To Ab Kettleby
Browns Hill
1879-81
1953-6
No2
Loco Shed
1930
1917
S
1926
1930
1924
To ASFORDBY
Old Hills Wood
To Melton Mowbray
To Long Clawson
To Eastwell
To Hickling
To Six Hills
H
1875
c1885
Loco Shed.
To Melton Mowbray
To Ab Kettleby
Holwell
Level Crossing
To Melton Mowbray
To ASFORDBY
Original layout at Holwell
Holwell Quarries
D - Davies.
H - Holwell.
S - Stanton (S&L Minerals from 1950).
Approximate limit of mined area.
Underground tramway.
IMG.

another three quarters of a mile south of the village bridge, and a fourth just south of Potter Hill. These bridges still survive (iron 'tank sides' on blue brick abutments), in one instance in open fields now. The branch was under construction from 1884 and the extension to Wycomb Junction in 1885/6 as recorded in Bradshaw's Railway Manual for these years (thanks to George Dow for this reference). The Holwell branch was officially opened for traffic on 1st January 1887 and the extension on 18th April 1887; the siding agreement with Holwell ironworks is dated 13th July 1887, according to ironworks records (thanks to Albert Bass and Paul Webb of Holwell Works for this information). Richard Dalgleish offered the quarry locomotive for sale in 1879, in which year Holwell ironworks was under construction and taking delivery of its first locomotive, the well-known Kitson, HOLWELL No. 1. It seems likely therefore that from 1879 to 1887 the traffic could have been worked by HOLWELL No. 1 or by a Midland Railway locomotive under a temporary arrangement. The extension commenced some 8 chains short of the terminus, but the latter was retained, at the end of a short branch line, as Holwell Wharf, an MR goods depot for miscellaneous traffic. Heavy engineering was a feature of the extension, starting off with a 70-foot cutting blasted through solid rock on a curve.

After 1881 the output went exclusively to Holwell ironworks, but by 1890 the best and most easily accessible stone had been got, and operations came to an end. A MR minute of 6th July 1888, in the records at Kew, refers to 'points necessary to connect the siding on the Holwell branch, where the Holwell Iron Company propose to construct on Midland land to the satisfaction of the Company engineer so that they can work a bed of ironstone at Scalford'. It seems that the proposal was not implemented. (thanks to Colin Aldworth for this item). The plant at the quarries (rails, wooden wagons etc) were transferred to the Eaton site.

The course of the BR branch is traceable throughout and it is interesting to note small changes that the MR made. The most obvious of these are of course the bridges mentioned above, accompanied by slight deviations of route of the roads or tracks crossed. There seem also to have been minor deviations taken by the MR line just north and south of Potter Hill. The section between Welby Bridge and Holwell Junction was obliterated by the development of the new Asfordby mine complex of the NCB in 1986. Of the narrow gauge tramways there are practically no tangible remains, which is hardly surprising, as the workings were purely surface ones and date from nearly a century ago. 'Holwell Huts' have been replaced by a substantial residence.

Footnotes

1. E. Wilson – 'The Lias Marlstone of Leicestershire as a source of iron'. The Midland Naturalist, 1885, p 61.
2. Staveley Board Minutes, 29th December 1874.
3. C.W. Barnes 'Holwell Ironworks' in 'The Stantonian', July 1936, p 136.

Grid References

720194	Standard gauge junction at Asfordby
736239	Holwell Huts
735240	Holwell Wharf junction
735239	Tipping dock
741245	The Willows
739244	Ironstone Farm
739242	Bridge under road (old tramway)

Locomotives

Gauge: 4ft 8½ins

–	0-4-OST	OC	HCR	187	1876	12 x 18ins	3ft 6ins		(a)	(1)
HOLWELL No. 1	0-6-OST	IC	K	1836	1879	14 x 20ins	3ft 6ins	New 2/1879	(b)	(2)

(a) New from HCR 6/1876; a rebuild of a locomotive by Thornewill & Warham
(b) Built 1872 but not purchased until 1879. Locomotive based at Holwell Ironworks

(1) Offered for sale 4/1879; s/s
(2) to Buckminster Quarries 1898

HOLWELL QUARRIES AND MINES

Owners: Stanton Ironworks Co Ltd: Stewarts & Lloyds Minerals Ltd from 1st January 1950.

The first Stanton ironworks were built by the canal at Stanton-by-Dale, near Ilkeston, in 1845; Hewlett records that ore was transported from Blisworth by canal from 1853 and the company obtained leases to work ironstone at Desborough and Wellingborough in the succeeding two decades. With the exception of Orton, no further properties in Northamptonshire were acquired until the business of James Pain Ltd was taken over in 1928. Marlstone ore was purchased from the Holwell Iron Co shortly after they started production in 1875 and a few years later the Stanton company decided to obtain their own concessions in the Leicestershire field, which were to supply them with the bulk of their home-produced ore for nearly half a century; and it was these Leicestershire quarries that set the pattern of Stanton's narrow gauge tramways that graced the scenes of their labours for so many years and now are no more.

The history of Stanton's Holwell workings is unusually complex, and full details of the transport arrangements will probably never be known; the account given of early days is based on Hewlett and the evidence of OS maps but is liable to revision. The quarries lay on the high ground east of the tiny secluded village of Holwell, and the first outcrop workings were on the edge of the escarpment, but later moved eastwards under deepening cover. According to Hewlett, operations commenced in 1879, south of the road from Holwell to Scalford Hall, on Brown's Hill, close by the old 'hills and dales' that marked the site of ancient pits of building stone. The output was conveyed by funicular down the hillside and tipped into trucks alongside the Holwell branch; at this time the latter was owned by the Holwell company, a competitor; but they had also been a supplier to Stanton and seem to have enjoyed cordial relations with them, so some arrangements were doubtless worked out. At the same time, ground about a half mile further north, south of 'The Willows' and adjoining the Holwell company's leases, had been leased to John Gilbert Crompton and George Crompton, two Stanton directors, who in 1881 leased their properties to the company, who transferred operations here from the Brown's Hill site.

A tramway was laid from the quarries along the south-eastern side of a small valley to a tipping dock alongside the Holwell branch adjacent to the level crossing with the Holwell-Scalford Hall road (the route of which was altered to cross the branch by a bridge, under Midland Railway auspices). This tramway was not a funicular, but climbed the slope obliquely at a moderate gradient, and was probably worked by gravity, with horses to haul up the empties; it may have been in operation before 1881 by the original owners, the Cromptons, but it did not last long, as the Stanton company dismantled the tippler and plant at Brown's Hill and re-erected it at the new site, with a straight funicular up the hillside to new workings about a quarter mile south of those near 'The Willows'. The tippler at the foot was at the same point as the later (lorry) tipping dock by the level crossing, and at the top of the incline the tramway passed beneath the very minor road from Brown's Hill to Ironstone Farm (to use the name appertaining later). Operations northeast of this road seem to have commenced in 1885 and presumably at this time the earlier tramway was dismantled; the geography suggests that side-tipping wagons were used, but the gauge of the metals is not known. The gauge of the funicular line is presumed to have been 1ft 9½ins; as we shall see, the system was later returned to the Brown's Hill site and was of that gauge then – and one so unusual is unlikely to have been adopted as new in 1917; it is almost certainly a product of early days when gauges were picked for local convenience without regard for standardization.

Quarrying was prosecuted on each side of the tramway and on both sides of the Brown's Hill-Ironstone Farm lane; on the southwest side, working ran from north to south and was completed in 1892, when permission was evidently obtained to close the lane in order to remove the ore beneath it, the lane being moved to a new alignment on the worked-out ground. Another diversion was of a bridleway, from Holwell village to the same lane, which was parallel to the earlier tramway and was moved to a new route 50-75 yards further west. In the twentieth century working continued further to the northeast, beyond the lane, up to 1917, when the outcrop was exhausted. The tramway equipment was then taken up again and relaid on the old Brown's Hill site, with the line extended from the top of the incline to open up fresh ground. Working commenced – recommenced, properly speaking – in 1917 near the cable drum, then moved anticlockwise, with the strips in succeeding years running roughly northwest-southeast.

The tramway was of 1ft 9½ins gauge and the incline of double track with two horizontal drums at the top mounted over the tracks, the chains running on rollers between the rails; descending loaded wagons hauled

Holwell Quarries & Mines. As the outcrop stone on Brown's Hill was nearing exhaustion, mining was started in 1931, and this view was taken before the introduction of diesel locomotive haulage in 1933. The need for the fence (see previous photograph) is obvious.

Stanton Ironworks Co Ltd

Holwell Quarries & Mines. Cable drum at the head of the narrow gauge incline down Brown's Hill, c. 1932. The perimeter fence is still there today, but enclosing a plantation.
Stanton Ironworks Co Ltd.

Holwell Quarries & Mines. Ruston & Hornsby 166046 shunting at the top of the incline, c. 1935. Note the different types of wagon. Ruston & Hornsby/IRS

up the empties. From the top of the incline to the quarries horses were used for hauling the small wooden tubs of about 10cwt capacity and of end-tipping type. By 1930 working under heavier cover was in progress and a small No. 14 type petrol-paraffin dragline was brought in to deal with it; but the overburden rapidly thickened and the bared ironstone surface was so irregular as to necessitate hand-cleaning. As an alternative, an experimental heading was driven to test the possibility of mining by 'pillar and stall' and this proved successful. Page Hackett, who worked at Holwell from 1921 to the end and possessed a phenomenal memory, quotes April 1931 for the opening of the mines and the year is confirmed by the survey maps; but some opencast quarrying continued up to 1933. Horses were used initially in the mines but were displaced by Ruston & Hornsby diesel locomotives by the end of 1933. The first one to arrive was a 16 horsepower machine that evidently was regarded as experimental, as it was designed to be capable of conversion to 2ft 4in gauge for use at Thingdon Mines, where it was sent a year later. The next locomotive, arriving in January 1934, was 10hp, but was re-engined to 18hp in 1937. A third locomotive, of 20hp, came in 1936. All were painted in standard Ruston livery of olive green with black and white lining; unlike the Thingdon locomotives, they were fitted with 'keyhole' cabs, as they worked as much (probably more) in the open than in the mines.

Eventually (about the end of 1942) the main mining gallery emerged at the abandoned face of the northern quarry site, and mining ceased shortly afterwards, in August 1943, with the resumption of opencast quarrying from the old site. To deal with the heavier overburden there was an influx of quarry machines – a 43RB excavator to open up the old face and to load three dumpers with spoil to fill in mine headings that had collapsed, a 21 RB to cut a new drain to keep water from flooding the new quarry, and a W90 electric walking dragline was erected on the site in the spring of 1945, with completion in June. During this preparatory period the narrow gauge tramway continued in use, the output being conveyed through the mine to the old incline and tippler, but it was obviously not capable of dealing with the much larger output made possible when the W 90 commenced removing overburden in 1946. The choice fell on lorry operation, the first of a series of such changes at Stanton's surviving narrow gauge ironstone tramways in Leicestershire. At Holwell it was also a case of history repeating itself in that the lorry route down to the Holwell branch was almost on the site of the former narrow gauge funicular from what was then the 'northern quarry'. Foundations were laid in October 1947 and the concrete tipping stage completed in the summer of 1948, lorries being used to cart foundation material for the road from the quarry; the surface was concreted. At the top of the incline the route had a 'kink' before crossing the Brown's Hill-Ironstone farm lane on the level and then running along the top of the ironstone face in the general direction of 'The Willows'. Two 5-ton Dennis tip-back lorries were purchased in 1948 (registered MNU 247, MNU 469) and commenced taking ore down the new roadway in the summer; a further lorry, this time an A.E.C. 'Monarch', RRB 665, arrived in September 1949. The tramway was lifted almost immediately the lorries took over and the two locomotives were sent to Buckminster shops, with the idea of using them at the Thistleton mines, but they were found to be under-powered for the work. The incline tippler and drum were dismantled and the area between the incline head and the blocked-up adit was planted with larches and other trees; the locomotive shed was taken down, but the concrete foundations were left in situ.

Holwell Quarries & Mines. No. 1 quarry, with an AEC 'Monarch' tipping lorry being loaded with calcined ore by a 43RB diesel dragline, on 2nd November 1953. BSC

Holwell Quarries & Mines. AEC lorry discharging its load at the new tipping dock on 2nd November 1953. This dock is close to the early tipping dock of the narrow gauge tramway of the 1880s. BSC

Operations in the quarry were now on a much larger scale than in the days of the tramway but were not especially remarkable, except that calcining of the ore on the quarry floor was introduced – the only place where calcining was done in the Marlstone in Leicestershire, as far as we know. The lorry road ran in a north-easterly direction to the main working face, known as No. 1 quarry, which was operated over the years in a clockwise direction from the terminus. In the course of time the face approached the 'green lane' (once part of a drover's road to Nottingham) from Scalford Hall to Brock Hill, and permission was sought to close off temporarily a section of the lane (which was very little used) to extend the quarry. While negotiations for this were in progress, No. 2 quarry, at Brown's Hill on the north side of the earlier workings, was opened to maintain continuous production, and was in use for three years, from the summer of 1953 to autumn 1956; it seems that the required permission to close off 'green lane' was not easily obtained! Work at No. 1 quarry was then resumed and continued up to October 1962 – only six years, so that the worked area beyond 'green lane' was only small. The lane from 'The Willows' to Scalford was also diverted by the provision of a straight road across an L-bend. It is worth noting that BSC records of the 'cessation of loading' quote the names of the two faces as 'Carter's' (closed in September 1962) and 'Crompton's (closed in October 1962) doubtless from the lessees east and west of 'green lane', with the name 'Crompton' going back to the original lessee of more than 80 years before.

With operations extending over 80 years, there are a number of points of interest in the remains at Holwell. The most recent quarrying areas, from 1948 to 1961 by lorry, automatically qualified for full restoration for the most part, i.e. after 1950, and this was done in 1974-6, when it was certain that reopening was not called for; the pre-1950 portion of No. 1 quarry nearer Brown's Hill was also treated similarly under a Government grant. The older quarrying areas on Brown's Hill itself, other than No.2 quarry, were excluded from these arrangements, and this is undoubtedly the most interesting section; furthermore, much of the area, including a half-mile stretch of the BR Holwell branch trackbed on each side of the incline foot, has been acquired by the Leicestershire & Rutland Trust for Nature Conservation as a nature reserve, and thus allowed to remain undisturbed. The course of the old incline can faintly be traced from the mound of stones that once raised the tippler above ground level, near the BR branch, and at the top of the hill there is a plantation of larch, pine and ash on the site of the quarries of the 1917-31 period; a few yards inside the fence, under heavy undergrowth, can be seen the concrete foundations of the locomotive shed, still with its inspection pit, and the course of the line to the blocked adit about one hundred yards from the shed, with the fence on the north side still in position. Northeast of this adit was the mining area passing under the road from Holwell to Scalford Hall; this was unfenced and the ground on both sides was pitted with 'sink holes' where the thin layer of boulder clay had fallen in on collapsed mines; following the publicity surrounding the accident suffered by some children exploring Thingdon mines, 62 of these 'sink holes' were filled in during the winter of 1975-6. The road carries warning notices of possible subsidences (1986). The fenced-off No. 2 quarry remains as it was left, the deep rock wall showing clearly that operations here were on a much more massive scale than the earlier ones, of which the final gullet, with bushes and larches, runs in a south-easterly direction parallel to the road. North of the adit is a tumbled area of rough tipping from No. 2 quarry, also fenced off. The adit was covered by an iron grille (1982), but there seems also to have been some recent quarrying, possibly for building stone. In 1991 the L & R NC laid paths to provide easier access and to reduce surface erosion.

Holwell Quarries & Mines. The foundations of the locomotive shed (for three Ruston & Hornsby locomotives) at Brown's Hill, with the trackbed leading towards the mine. This view is in almost the same spot as the photograph of the cable drum, and was taken on 4th April 1953, since when the whole area has been covered by a plantation; but the shed foundations and the cutting are still to be seen. Eric Tonks

Holwell Quarries & Mines. In 1942 the mines tramway emerged into the earlier quarrying area north of Brown's Hill, and opencast quarrying took place,with the output being conveyed through the mine to the incline top. As quarrying on a more massive scale was introduced, lorries were brought in to take the output to a new tipping stage on the other side of the road bridge over the BR branch. This ironstone face is still visible, but the entrance has been filled in apart from a small section at the top so that bats may roost in the old mines. 4th April 1953. Eric Tonks

Holwell Quarries & Mines. No. 1 quarry, 15th March 1958, showing from left to right – the 'High Wall'; the lorry road on top of the ironstone bed; calcining on the quarry floor; and worked-out ground. Dragline in the distance. BSC

Brown's Hill is a very pleasant spot in which to ramble – there is plenty to see and speculate upon; north of the railway bridge there are also things to see but the area is less attractive visually. The lorry tipping dock was still present in 1982[1] and its associated concrete road is overgrown on the lower slope, but clearer higher up the hill, and across the road we come to No 1. quarry; just inside the gate is a timber merchant's yard, and behind that a small portion of the old ironstone face where was the mine exit, now sealed off. A continuation of this face is visible south of the road. The most spectacular reminder here is the final face of the overburden, at the foot of which ran the lorry road to the working area near 'The Willows'. This length of almost vertical cliff, a third of a mile long and up to 40 feet high, was universally known as 'The High Wall' and was of great interest to geologists as a unique Liassic section; accordingly the Leicestershire & Rutland Trust for Nature Conservation asked permission for it to be preserved instead of being smoothed over in the usual way, and Ministerial permission for this was granted in the summer of 1976. The lorry road remains for access but the rest of No. 1 quarry has been smoothed over completely and returned to cultivation. The original adit was filled in (note the different appearance from the rest of the face) but the top left open, with a concrete surround and iron bars, so that bats might roost in the old mines in peace (1982). Possibly the stone filling came from No. 2 quarry (see above).

Where the quarry crossed the route of the 'green lane' the ground was restored – the dip in the ground is still very obvious – and the route replaced by a footpath alongside a new hedge between two wire fences. The 'cutoff' on the minor road to Scalford from 'The Willows' remains, with its wire fences indicating the change of route. At the Scalford Hall end however walkers are still deterred from entering by the fence erected during the closure, and other impedimenta. However, the right-of-way is presumed still to exist, as the BSC were required to reinstate the footpath – and the route is clear throughout.

Of the earliest quarrying areas dating from 1881-1917 only indirect traces remain, but they are there and can be seen from the Scalford Hall-Ironstone Farm road. Between the point where the second tramway (inclined) went beneath this road, a few yards north of the lorry crossing, and the point where the earlier tramway crossed the lane, the hedge of the east side (there is no hedge on the west side) is plain hawthorn; south of this section the hedges contain trees and to the north the hedges also include wild hops, indicating that they are of long standing. Between these two points the lane also dips slightly at each end, showing that the ore below the surface was removed and the road displaced westwards, as already described. The fields are also at a similar level. 'The Willows' is probably much as it was in Victorian times, and there are still willows by the pond; the ground nearby is hummocky in a 'gridiron' pattern suggesting one time disturbance, and one hedge has been replaced by a wire fence. Near the junction of this lane with that from Scalford Hall is a relatively new building called Ironstone Farm, and in the field behind it is a large square iron water tank on brick arches; it was originally filled by a windmill, replaced later by an electric pump. Immediately north of the lorry route from the tippler, the course of the tramway funicular can be picked out by the disturbed ground of the hillside, this being best observed from the road through the village. The old quarry area near this route is now arable land.

Footnotes

1. Permission to demolish this had been sought in December 1963, but was apparently not received.

Grid References

740234	'Old Hill and Dale'
739235	Tipping dock south of MR bridge
740235	Top of incline
738237	Tipping dock north of MR bridge
740238	Top of incline
739241	Level crossing (old tramway)
740234	Locomotive shed, Browns Hill
741234	Tunnel to No.1 quarry, by loco. shed
742237	Tunnel to No.1 quarry, at quarry
739235	Lorry tipping dock
745240	'High Wall' -north end
746240	New footpath crossing site at north end of green lane.

Locomotives

Gauge: 1ft 9½ins

–	4wDM	RH 168831	1933	16HP	Class	2¾ tons	New 11/1933	(1)
No. 1	4wDM	RH 166046	1934	10HP (18HP from 1927)	Class	2½tons	New 1/1934	(2)
No. 2	4wDM	RH 179003	1936	20HP	Class	2¾ tons	New 5/1936	(2)

(1) to Thingdon Mines c 10/1934
(2) to Buckminster Workshops 9/1948

Quarry Machines

	No. 4	PP. Dragline	RH 1200	1927	⅜ Cu. Yds.	40ft.	(a)	(1)
No. 203	43RB	D. Dragline. Crawler	RB 4763	1939	1½ Cu. Yds.	50ft.	(b)	(2)
	21RB	D. Dragline	RB 2511	1934	¾ Cu. Yds.	40ft.	(c)	(3)
	43RB	D. Dragline. Crawler	RB 3015	1936	¾ Cu. Yds.	60ft.	(d)	(4)
No. 205	W90	E. Walking Dragline	R&R 1693	1945	1½ Cu. Yds.	127ft.	New(e)	(5)
	21RB	E. Dragline. Caterpillar	RB 3679	1937	¾ Cu. Yds.	40ft.	(f)	(6)
	10RB	D. Clamshell Dragline	RB 3282	1936	⅚ Cu. Ft.	35ft.	(g)	(7)

(a) ex Buckminster Quarries c 1930
(b) ex Woolsthorpe Quarries 1/1943.
Later 1¼ Cu. Yds., 60ft.
(c) ex Tilton Quarries 6/1943
(d) ex Market Overton Quarries 3/1944.
Later 1½ Cu. Yds. 40ft.
(e) Erected 3-5/1945 on site. New 9/1943 per R&R records
(f) ex Glendon Quarries 3/1946
(g) ex Buckminster Quarries 6/1947

(1) to Holwell Ironworks 8/1948. then to South Witham Quarries
(2) at No. 2 qy. To Stanton Ironworks c 1967
(3) to Wellingborough Quarries 6/1945
(4) to Market Overton Quarries 9/1944
(5) at No. 1 qy. to Woolsthorpe Quarries c 1962
(6) to Nuthall Sandpits, Nottinghamshire 8/1948
(7) to Wirksworth Quarries, Derbyshire 10/1947

HOLWELL QUARRIES
Owner: E.P. Davis

The Midland Railway built their Holwell branch, on the course of the Holwell Iron Co's tramway, in the middle 1880s and also the Holwell extension to join at Wycomb Junction the recently opened Great Northern Railway complex of mineral branches to Waltham, Eastwell and Eaton. The Extension was not easy to build, and immediately north of Holwell village was taken through an impressive rocky cutting, at the south end of which it joined the course of the original Holwell branch a couple of hundred yards or so short of the terminus at Holwell Wharf, this last remaining as a branch. The combined Holwell branch and extension was opened to traffic in 1887 and it was probably because of the change of status of this line that E.P. Davis, proprietor of Bennerley Furnaces, in the Erewash Valley, opened his quarries in the vicinity of Holwell Mouth (a chalybeate spring) north-west of the village; while the branch was owned by the Holwell Iron Co, the latter might not have agreed to convey Davis's output.

Operations commenced in 1888 at the outcrop or very near to it, from which the ore was conveyed over a three-foot gauge tramway to an elevated tipping dock along the south-west side of the Wharf; motive power was provided by two horses hired locally, according to 'The Geology of the Melton Mowbray district and south-east Nottinghamshire' by G. W. Lamplugh, C.B. Wedd, R.L. Sherlock and B. Smith, 1909. It seems likely that the line ran along the west side of the gated lane from Holwell to the crossroads with the Six Hills-Belvoir road, and beyond that dividing into branches in each direction along the outcrop; a shelf by the lane-side south of the crossroads suggests that this was the trackbed, and the southern end of this shelf is in line with Holwell Wharf. Some quarrying was also carried out just south of the Six Hills road, and the last working was a quarter-mile further south, between the Six Hills road and

Nursery Lane; a branch tramway was put in to reach this and the line to the other pits was lifted. The workings were very shallow, hence not recorded in LQ, but Hewlett gives the closure date as 1908, when the tramway was lifted. For the same reason, there are virtually no traces of them; nor of the tramway apart from the possible lane-side section mentioned. Modest earthworks record the site of the former tipping dock at the Wharf, which was closed completely on 2nd June 1958. The immediate Wharf site has been in the occupation of the Wright family since quarrying started.

Grid References

733241	Tipping dock, Holwell Wharf
731244	Level crossing, Six Hills road.

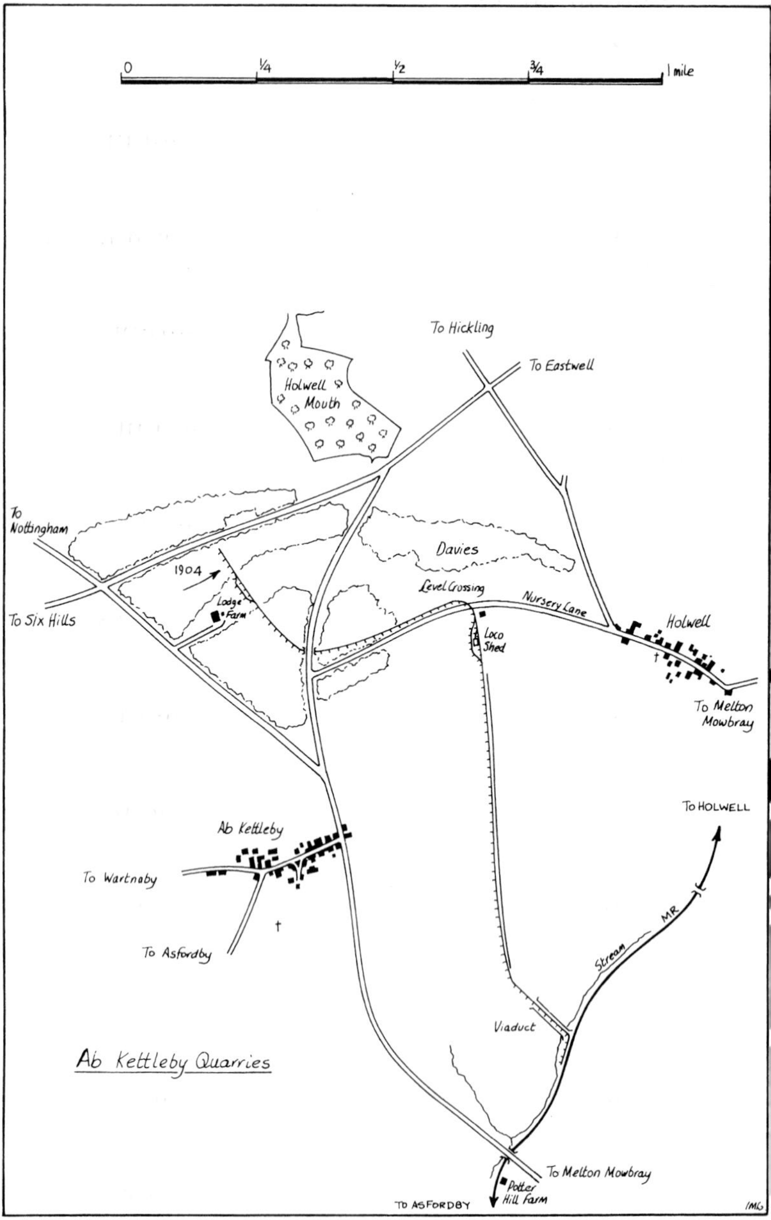
0
1/4
1/2
3/4
1 mile
Holwell Mouth
To Hickling
To Eastwell
To Nottingham
Davies
1904
To Six Hills
Lodge Farm
Level Crossing
Nursery Lane
Loco Shed
Holwell
To Melton Mowbray
To HOLWELL
Ab Kettleby
To Wartnaby
To Asfordby
MR
Stream
Viaduct
Ab Kettleby Quarries
To Melton Mowbray
Potter Hill Farm
TO ASFORDBY
IMG

AB KETTLEBY QUARRIES
Owners: Holwell Iron Co Ltd

E.P. Davis's quarries lay on the outcrop east of Holwell Mouth, and the ground to the west as far as the Melton Mowbray-Nottingham road was worked by the Holwell Iron Co Ltd as part of their Ab Kettleby quarries; west of the main road were Stanton's Wartnaby quarries. The last were opened in 1879, Davis's pits in 1888 and Ab Kettleby in 1892, thus completing the development of the outcrop in this area. Holwell Mouth is a deep gash in the escarpment caused by the continual flow of water from the spring over many millenia, and the associated destructive forces of nature; in the course of this the Marlstone Rock bed has been worn away at this point, the declivity starting at the Six Hills road. The lease from the Duke of Rutland included the area near the escarpment north of the Six Hills-Belvoir road, and also a considerable area south of the road, including a triangle of land round Lodge Farm and, further east, ground north of Nursery Lane. Operations commenced in 1892, two years after the closure of the company's quarries north of Holwell village, and the new quarries were served by a tramway about one mile in length and of considerable interest, with one portion worked by locomotives, a cable-operated incline, and a timber viaduct.

Output from the quarries was conveyed to the head of the incline south of Nursery Lane (Holwell-Ab Kettleby); most of the quarries were north of this lane, which was crossed on the level, but there was also a line at one time to a quarry south of the lane and north-east of Ab Kettleby village. There was also a tunnel beneath the Melton Mowbray-Long Clawson lane to pits on the west side. South of the level crossing were the locomotive shed, carpenter's shop, blacksmith's shop and office – a bungalow of wood and 'tin' (presumably corrugated iron): this information was provided by Page Hackett. The incline was half a mile long at a gradient of about 1 in 24, and it and the lower portion of the tramway were of double track, and haulage was by cable to which the wooden end-tipping wagons were clipped singly. At the foot of the incline the tramway was carried over a wooden viaduct 500 feet long and about 25 feet high at the highest point where it crossed the stream, and then turned south on to an elevated bank twenty feet high parallel to the Holwell branch at Potter Hill on the north side of the Nottingham road. The precise method of tipping is not known; presumably the wagons at the end of the viaduct tipped their contents into a railway wagon below and were then taken

Ab Kettleby Quarries. The higher level portion of the 2ft 8 1/2ins gauge tramway leading to the quarries was worked by two secondhand locomotives. Fortunately a photograph of one of them has survived, taken presumably when at Holwell Works. She is by Dick & Stevenson, a rare make. BSC

back and put on the elevated siding for return to the pits. The tramway was of the unusual gauge of 2ft 8½in, the origin of which is unknown; in mid-Victorian times hundreds of industrial lines were laid to gauges selected simply to suit the work, but as ownership of industrial installations came into the hands of a smaller number of larger companies, the value of standardisation became increasingly apparent and the selection of 'odd' gauges rarer. It is possible that the Ab Kettleby gauge arose from the availability of a cheap locomotive, but it is more likely that horses were used at first. Certainly, when the company advertised for a locomotive in 1896/97 either as a spare to one they already had or to commence locomotive traction, they had great difficulty in getting one. Five such advertisements are known in the trade press of the day, with the emphasis on cheapness.

An advertisement in Contract Journal of 7th August 1907 states that 'A.T. & E.A. Crow are to sell on 9th August for Holwell Iron Co Ltd at Abb Kettleby Mines (now closed) . . . two tank locomotives 0-4-0 with cylinders 10 x 12ins (? 10ins and 12ins) gauge 2ft 8ins. (sic) by Hawthorn Leslie and Dick & Stevenson.' By a stroke of luck a photograph of the latter has survived; it appeared in 'The Stantonian' and shows her to be a 0-4-0 ST with square saddle tank, no cab, weatherboard or rear sheet, inclined cylinders, solid wheels, connecting rods inside the side rods and other unusual features. She was titled HOLWELL No. 7 on brass plates of standard Holwell design and was clearly second-hand. The identity of the 'Hawthorn Leslie' has not been established, the most likely contender by this firm (who built few narrow gauge locomotives) being their number 1901, again second-hand. 'Hawthorn Leslie' *might* be a mistake for Hawthorns of Leith (the advertisement seems to have been somewhat carelessly put together), another obscure Scottish builder like Dick & Stevenson. One of the locomotives is said to have been named VICTORIA – presumably the Hawthorn – the plates having possibly been transferred from MW 589 when the latter became HOLWELL No. 11.

The quarries were closed in 1907 and the locomotives disposed of to unknown purchasers, but the track and wagons were sent to South Witham limestone quarries, where they saw considerable service. It will be noted that this seemed to be Holwell's standard practice, the Holwell quarry equipment going to Eaton, and that from Ab Kettleby to South Witham. As with Davis's Holwell pits, there is almost nothing to be seen today apart from the lowered fields around Lodge Farm; some of the buildings by the level crossing were converted into dwellings, but these

Ab Kettleby Quarries. The quarries were on high ground and the tramway descended a half-mile incline, crossed a stream by a viaduct, and ended on an embankment alongside the Holwell branch. One wagon frame was still there on 8th October 1986, and has survived 80 years after the closure. Eric Tonks

have been replaced by modern bungalows. The course of the line is quite impossible to trace; the viaduct has disappeared entirely but the mound of red earth alongside the railway siding site at Potter Hill still stands with, on the top, the remains of an upturned wagon. The wooden top is decayed but the frame is intact and there is an axle and one pair of wheels with six curved spokes; the gauge is 2ft 7ins minimum – suggesting a gauge of anything from 2ft 7½in to 2ft 8½in. Along the Six Hills road is a brick building with a corrugated asbestos roof, a wide wooden door facing Holwell and a bricked-up window each side; this was an implement shed for the estate farm and had no connection with the ironstone workings.

Grid References

732524	Tipping dock, Potter HIll
730237	Locomotive shed
731236	Top of incline
723240	'Shed' by road (not ironstone)

Locomotives

Gauge: 2ft 8½ins

VICTORIA	0-4-OT	OC	HL (?)			(1)
HOLWELL No. 7	0-4-0ST	OC	Dick & Stevenson	(14) (?)	1868 (?)	(1)

(1) Offered for sale 8/1907. s/s

WARTNABY QUARRIES
Owners: Stanton Ironworks Co Ltd

Wartnaby quarries were the westernmost of those on the Marlstone Cliff and the stone was of a richness comparable with that at Holwell; and development commenced very shortly after Holwell. In 1878 J.G. Crompton and G. Crompton, both directors of the Stanton Ironworks Co Ltd, leased from the Bingham family of Wartnaby Hall and the March family of Wartnaby Castle a considerable area north of the village, from the vicinity of 'Stonepit House' at the western end to the Melton Mowbray-Nottingham road at the east, on both sides of the Six Hills-Belvoir road. The leases were later transferred to the Stanton company in the same way as the Holwell quarries. The workings eventually covered almost all the land over the 500-foot contour between these extremities, about one mile from east to west and a half mile north to south; there was also a very small area east of Wartnaby just below 500 feet. The stone was outcrop, easily accessible by manual labour, and no quarry machines were ever used.

The quarries were about equidistant from Holwell Wharf and from the Midland Railway Nottingham line, which was opened for goods traffic on 1st November 1879; but connection to the latter was simpler topographically, and a tramway of three-feet gauge was laid along the top of the Marlstone Cliff to within a third of a mile of the MR Old Dalby tunnel, then obliquely down the slope at a gradient of about 1-in-15 to a tipping dock on the north side of a set of sidings off the Midland line close to the northern portal of the tunnel; the distance from the tipping dock to the nearest quarry was just under one mile. The wagons were shallow end-tippers of wood, and were probably unloaded from a plate-tippler. The incline was operated by cable from a drum at the head, where also were the locomotive shed and a smithy. Beyond the shed the line curved east-north-east in a shallow cutting, then on an embankment and bridge to carry it over the Nether Broughton-Saxilby road; this was the only ironstone overbridge known apart from those at Oxfordshire Ironstone. The line then turned east in another shallow cutting towards the Six Hills road by a group of buildings referred to as 'Stonepit House' – doubtless so named after a quarry used for building stone. The quarries started here, and the tramways beyond were altered to suit production requirements.

Production commenced in 1879 under the management of Walter G. Fowler; horse traction was used first along the high line, but locomotive

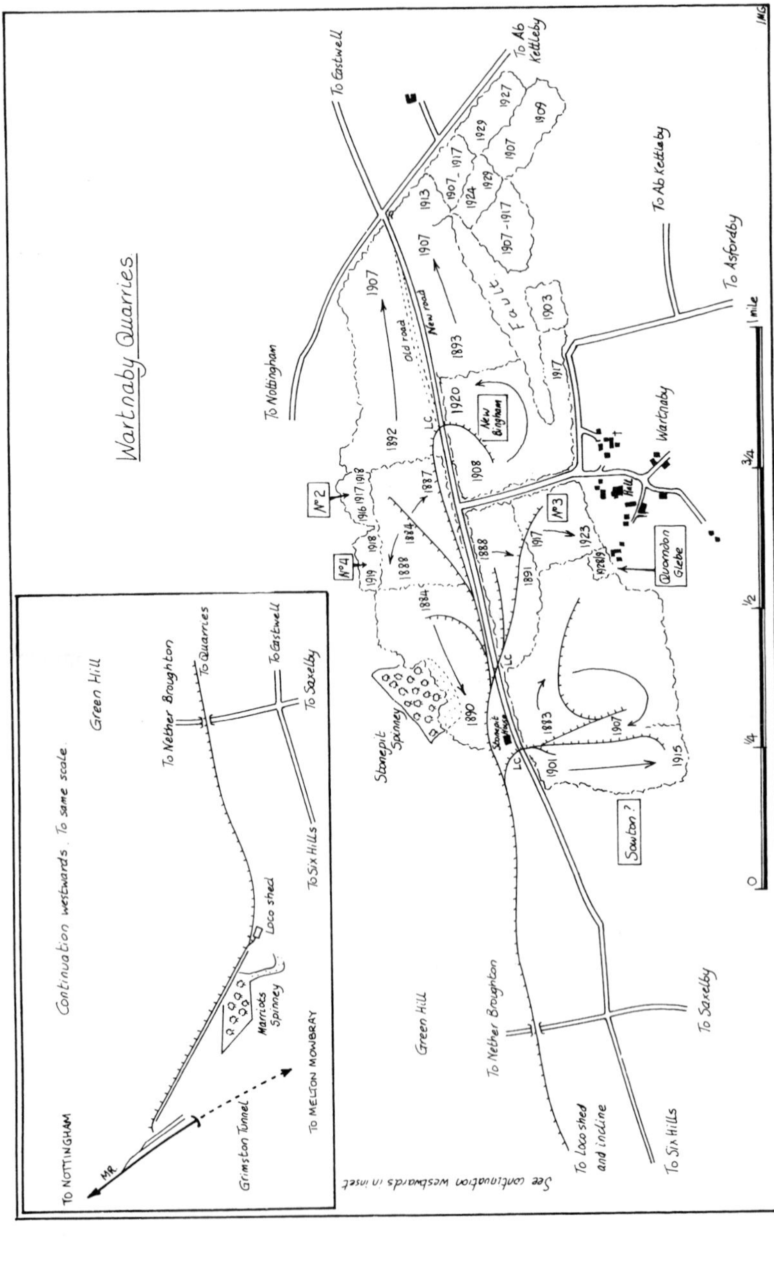
Wartnaby Quarries.
Continuation westwards. To same scale.
See continuation westwards in inset
To Nottingham
To Eastwell
To Ab Kettleby
To Asfordby
To Saxelby
To Six Hills
To Nether Broughton
To Loco shed and incline
Green Hill
Stonepit Spinney
Stonepit House
Wartnaby
Hall
Quorndon Glebe
New Bingham
Sowton ?
No 2
No 3
No 4
Fault
Old road
New road
LC
0
1/4
1/2
3/4
1 mile
TO NOTTINGHAM
MR
Grimston Tunnel
TO MELTON MOWBRAY
Marriots Spinney
Loco shed
To Quarries
To Eastwell
IMG

power was introduced in 1880, according to Hewlett. As with all quarries under Stanton ownership, the locomotive stock was never static, one sent to works for repair being replaced by another fresh from the shops and probably from another quarry; it follows that, since records of early allocations have been destroyed, there may have been here at various times engines other than those in the list, which has been compiled in the main from official sources that did not extend before World War I. In early years the locomotives were simply titled STANTON No. X and some were always so numbered, while others were later given names, either of girls or associated with the quarry where they were working at the time; officially however they were always referred to by number. A curiosity in this respect is the Bagnall side tank BOTTESFORD, whose name suggests associations with the Brewer's Grave tramway at Woolsthorpe, served by Bottesford GNR siding, though in fact it never (as far as is known) worked there. In old Stanton records the engine is referred to as No. 7, though whether this title was actually carried is unknown; the name BOTTESFORD was merely painted on, as was the company custom in earlier years, cast brass plates being a later introduction sometimes coinciding with the exchange of names for numbers. Latterly indeed BOTTESFORD was the only Stanton ironstone locomotive without a brass plate. Its acquisition of this inappropriate name therefore seems a mystery; possibly it was intended to go to Brewer's Grave at one time and given the name in anticipation of a transfer that did not materialise.

At Wartnaby two locomotives were the normal allocation – one only up to 1882 and from March 1928. The first engine was STANTON No. 9, an 0-4-2T built by John Fowler & Co Ltd. of Leeds, most of whose steam locomotive production went overseas. She was unique to the ironstone fields and the main recollections preserved are of her misdemeanours. She was referred to by the staff simply as 'The Fowler'. It might be mentioned, incidentally, that BOTTESFORD is quoted in one of Bagnall's records as having been delivered to W.C. Fowler & Co. STANTON No. 9 was sent to Woolsthorpe when the neat little Hudswell Clarke arrived and from then until March 1928 six-coupled locomotives were the rule, in keeping with the two-mile trip each way that they mostly had to work. The liveries of these engines are described under other quarries where they worked as in any case information direct from Wartnaby is scanty.

The earliest workings were immediately beyond Stonepit House, north of the road and towards the edge of the Cliff, i.e. at the outcrop, with the working face moving eastwards and the tramway extended along the north side of the road as required; there was also working west of the initial pit in 1889/90, north of Stonepit House. A branch line was put in, crossing the road on the level a hundred yards west of Stonepit House to open up quarries on the south side, where development took place from 1888 onwards. On this south side there were two areas that were developed simultaneously, west and east of the road to Wartnaby village. The west side was opened up from the level crossing, mainly working clockwise; on the east side another branch from the main tramway crossed the Six Hills road 100 yards east of the junction with the road to the village, and the ground then worked north to south in strips eastwards from 1892. About the turn of the century this portion of the Six Hills road was diverted a few yards to a parallel course to the south so that the original road could yield up its underlying stone in further strips up to 1907, when the border of the main Nottingham road was reached. The tramway was then on the north side of the Six Hills road; a tramway was laid south of the road later to reach the ground there.

Later developments filled in the gaps left by previous operations, most of them south of the Six Hills road – one area west of the first level crossing by Stonepit House (1902-15), east of the road to Wartnaby village (1909-20), west of the same road (1917 onwards – No. 3 Pit); and finally the furthest east alongside the main Nottingham road (1907 onwards). At the western end of the chain of workings, a further 10 acres were leased for 10 years from 25th March 1910 from the Ecclesiastical Commissioners as part of their Quorndon Glebe Estate; a narrow strip running north-north-east from the boundary of Wartnaby Hall Park, and the main block a half mile to the west, and south of Stonepit House. The latter area was worked as part of the advancing face at the western end of operations, but a five-year extension of the lease was obtained to enable the narrow strip to be dealt with. The earlier history of Quorndon Glebe is dealt with in the next section. The area in the angle between the Nottingham road and the Six Hills road was leased from Leicester Hospital, according to a note on the surveyor's plans, but details of the lease are not known.

A minor but interesting point concerns the large field in the angle between the Six Hills road and the west side of the road to the village. Along both road-sides was a narrow belt of trees, and when quarrying of this field commenced in 1890 at the north side, the trees along the Six Hills road were left, possibly to screen Wartnaby Hall from the road. Quarrying halted about a year later but was resumed in 1917, working clockwise towards the village; but in this case the roadside trees were

Wartnaby Quarries. Although the top of the chimney is missing, we include this photograph as the only known one of a locomotive at Wartnaby. She is clearly Bagnall 1272 but appears to carry no title; see text for discussion of the name BOTTESFORD carried by the locomotive elsewhere.
G. Rigby/RRM Archives

sacrificed, possibly because of the exigencies of war. Today the line of trees bordering the Six Hills road stands on slightly elevated ground suggesting a former tramway embankment, but the fact is that the trees are on the old ground level, the rest of the field having been quarried away. The hedge alongside the village road is a simple, probably replacement, one.

Two small faces north of the Six Hills road were worked last in World War I: these were near the outer edge of the outcrop near the escarpment, that had been ignored in early days for some reason. The western face was known as No. 4 Pit (worked 1918-19) and the eastern as No. 2 Pit (worked 1916-18). In the post World War I period demand was slack and at Wartnaby, like everywhere else, production was reduced; a small pocket at the edge of Wartnaby Hall grounds was finished in 1923 (including the small strip of the Quorndon Glebe lease) and thereafter strips of ground were worked close to the main Nottingham road. LI states that the last workings were'immediately north of Wartnaby' (i.e. by Wartnaby Hall), possibly an extension of the 1923 site. This would accord with the period 1928-29 when HARSTON was the sole locomotive, as the shorter distance would be within the compass of the 0-4-0ST whereas the full distance to the Nottingham road probably was not. Quarrying came to an end in 1929 with the virtual exhaustion of all the available outcrop stone; on all sides the ground falls away from the Wartnaby plateau and no stone occurs.

The numbers or names of the early working faces are not known; the earliest record in GSM refers to the Pits Nos. 2, 3 and 4 mentioned above, and as these were opened respectively 1916-17-18 it seems pretty certain that they refer only to that period and have no reference to the adjoining worked-out areas. The surveyor's plans show that No. 4 pit was on land owned by Captain Bingham. GSM also refers to the New Bingham Pit for the later (1917-20) workings east of the road to the village, but as this had been worked continually from 1907 the name may well have been in use before 1917. Early quarries may possibly have been called Bingham No. 1, March No. 1, etc., but we are only guessing here. Towards the end, Page Hackett recalls Sowton Pit – the Quorndon Glebe area at the extreme south-west; and Bishop Pit (possibly the other Glebe area north of Wartnaby Hall?).

Considering that these workings have been closed for half a century, it is quite remarkable how much has survived; not much can be seen of the quarries themselves apart from shallow depressions in the fields, but the main tramway route is traceable virtually from end to end. Nothing of the tipping dock at Old Dalby can be seen, but the formation of the incline is still perfectly clear all the way to the summit, where it cuts through a corner of Marriott's Spinney. In 1982 the fields on both sides of the trackbed had been ploughed up, but the latter, with some bushes growing on it, had been left. On the level ground by the trees is the locomotive shed, with a small pond at the side, and also traces of the foundations of the 'smithy' shown on the 6in. OS map. The locomotive shed itself is of unusual construction. Along each side are four cast iron cylindrical pillars with small horizontal girders between them; iron-framed windows of 20 panes are set in wooden frames, three to each side, the remainder of the wall space being occupied by black corrugated iron. The doors are of wood, a large one facing the quarries and a small one at the rear. The roof is of corrugated asbestos, doubtless replacing corrugated iron of earlier days, and there is only one 'pot' – now gone – that seems to have fitted over a louvre, as the shed had space for two engines. Unfortunately, the building has gradually deteriorated over the years and by 1979 half of the north wall had fallen down. The situation is delightful, with the belt of trees behind the shed building, the pond, and to the north the brush-covered escarpment commanding a magnificent view over the Vale of Belvoir. What a site for a photograph of a narrow gauge locomotive shunting wagons at the head of the incline!

Beyond the buildings the shallow cutting is now partly filled with trees and bushes – with some newly planted in 1982 – and the embankment further along is overgrown, too. The bridge over the Nether Broughton-Saxilby road has long since been pulled down and the embankment on the west side has been removed for a few yards for cultivation, and no longer reaches the road. On the east side the grassy embankment continues with another wonderful view over the Vale before the route turns east in a shallow cutting towards the Six Hills road; another pond is passed and the line enters a grove of trees and finally reaches the road by the group of buildings at Stonepit House; just west of this a branch crossed the road by a level crossing, the site of which is between two modern bungalows. Of the purely quarry lines there are no traces at all other than fields a little below ground level at various points. This is not surprising of course; on the other hand, there are a couple of warnings concerning interpretation of the remains. There is a belt of trees stretching about 250 yards on the south side of the Six Hills road west of the turning to Wartnaby village; the explanation of the 'embankment' on which they stand has already been given. There is another belt of trees, north of the road, stretching a quarter mile westwards from its junction with the Nottingham road. These trees do not appear on the OS maps and have obviously been planted since quarrying ceased – and as the road has been quarried as well, there is not even a drop in level to suggest quarrying. Of the road diversion there is not any recognisable sign.

This system must assuredly have been one of the most scenic of the ironstone lines, and it is to be regretted that only one quarry photograph (in 1908) appears to have survived, in the collection of the Institute of Geological Sciences; this tantalising view (included in Part 1) shows very clearly the barrow-and-plank system of working typical of the period, also the type of wagon, but of the locomotive only a plume of smoke from beyond a bend in the quarry wall; and a distant hedge with, perhaps, the Vale of Belvoir below. How we wish there were more! In the winter, with a keen north wind blowing up the Cliff, it would have been a pretty cold spot – hence perhaps the trees – but there were summers as well as winters. It is fortunate that information and records, and traceable remains survive to remind us of the past.

Grid References

684235	Tipping dock, Old Dalby
689235	Top of incline
689233	Locomotive shed
696234	Bridge over Saxilby road
706235	Level crossing by Stonepit House
704234	Level crossing to eastern quarries
709235	Line of trees, unexcavated, west end
713237	Diversion of road, east end

Locomotives

Gauge: 3ft 0ins

STANTON No. 9	0-4-2T	OC	JF	3866	c 1880	7 x ins		New c 1880	(1)
STANTON No. 10	0-6-0ST	OC	HC	235	1882	9 x 15ins	2ft 6ins	New 5/1882	(2)
STANTON No. 7	0-6-0T	OC	WB	1272	1890	9 x 13½ins	2ft 2ins	New 6/1890	(3)
STANTON No. 12	0-6-0ST	OC	HC	429	1894	9½ x 15ins	2ft 6ins.	(a)	(4)
HARSTON	0-4-0ST	OC	WB	1587	1900	9 x 14ins	2ft 3½ins	(b)	(5)

(a) ex Woolsthorpe (Brewers Grave) Quarries c 1900
(b) ex Rothwell Hill Quarries, 3/1928

(1) to Woolsthorpe (Brewers Grave) Quarries 11/1883

(2) to Woolsthorpe (Brewers Grave) Quarries c 1900; ex Woolsthorpe (Harston) Quarries 4/1924; to Holwell Works 7/1927; to Harston Quarries 8/1928
(3) to Holwell Works 3/1928; to Tilton Quarries 3/1929
(4) to Holwell Works 4/1924; to Eaton Quarries 5/1925
(5) to Eaton Ropeway Quarries 1/1931

WARTNABY QUARRIES
Owners: J. & W.K. Birkinshaw

The only documentary evidence known to us of these workings (or indeed of the firm) is a file in the Leicestershire Record Office which appears to have come from a solicitor's office in Loughborough, and appertains to the Quorndon Glebe Estate of the Ecclesiastical Commissioners. The latter included land at Wartnaby, 22 acres of which were leased to J. & W.K. Birkinshaw for 15 years from 7th June 1883. Birkinshaw's official notepaper gives the office address as 30 Charnwood Street, Derby (confirmed in 'Kelly's Directory' as occupied by Joseph Birkinshaw) and describes them as iron ore proprietors with mines at Old Dalby and Desborough, neither of which is mentioned in MS nor positively identified. In the case of the Quorndon lease it seems doubtful if this was ever worked; as their Land Agent, Charles Woolley explained in a letter of 2nd May 1885 to the Ecclesiastical Commissioners, because of the depressed state of the iron trade they had only worked ironstone on the adjoining estate to about one third of that expected, and asked for a reduction in rent and an extension of time for the lease – both of which were granted, the lease for a further six years. In the last of several subsequent letters, dated 8th January 1891, Birkinshaws stated that they 'should begin to work this year', but it seems unlikely that they did so. Going by the previous correspondence, they did work an adjoining area, but just where this was and for how long they operated, are unknown; they could even have commenced before Stanton did, but it is clear that they were only in a small way of business, and probably carted the output to Old Dalby station, where they presumably had an office. On 6th January 1891, George C. Bond enquired on behalf of Staveley for the leasing of ironstone on the Quorndon Estate, but nothing transpired; but in 1910 Stanton leased 10 acres, as described in the preceding section; in this case the area concerned is known precisely but whether it was part of the original Birkinshaw lease of 22 acres is not stated – but very possibly it was.

Wartnaby Quarries. These quarries were closed in 1929 after 50 years of operation, and the buildings at the top of the incline were mostly left intact. Shown here is the engine shed, photographed in August 1962. Since then most of the corrugated iron sheets have been blown down, and only the framework of the shed remains. Mr. Hurst

Wartnaby Quarries. The trackbed of the tramway is still visible from the top of the incline at its western end. This view was taken on 23rd February 1969, east of the locomotive shed.
P.D. Rowbotham

THE EATON AREA

The development of Eaton as an ironstone quarrying centre bore a number of parallels with that at Holwell; the village lies in a hollow of the hills and in the course of time was surrounded on all sides by quarries connected by tramways mostly, but not all, to mineral branches of main line railways. As with Holwell, development was by a number of operators and even when in later years the quarries were all controlled by Stewards & Lloyds Minerals Ltd and Staveley Minerals Ltd, the piecemeal approach was still apparent in the variety of transport systems. This was brought about to a large extent by geographical peculiarities. The ironstone occurs over the area from the top of the Marlstone Cliff (about 500 feet O.D.) southward to the foot of the Oolitic Cliff (about 400 feet O.D.) mostly as outcrop or under thin cover; but the region is much dissected by valleys carved by the river Devon and its tributaries that have removed the ironstone stratum in the process. One prehistoric valley running north to south between Eastwell and Eaton has been filled with Boulder Clay by a retreating glacier of the Ice Age; the difference in soil is apparent in the vegetation, and of course no ironstone is present.

The area is sparsely inhabited and at the time of the opening up of Holwell there were no railways within reasonable distance – hence the construction of mineral lines, providing one of the few examples where ironstone entered the sphere of railway politics. Just how far ironstone interests were directly involved is a matter for conjecture, but indirectly they certainly played a part. D.L. Franks, in his 'Great Northern and London & North Western Joint Railway' (Turntable Enterprises, Leeds, 1974), gives a detailed account of the complex inter-company wrangling preceding the construction of this cross-country line that never boasted a flourishing passenger service but survived because of the ironstone traffic. Less than three years after the line from Bottesford to Melton Mowbray was opened to traffic on 1st July 1878, the Eastwell Iron Ore Co commenced building their tramway to Stathern ironstone sidings; but all the other quarries in the Eaton district were served by the mineral system built by the Great Northern Railway. The Holwell Iron Co obtained a lease to work ironstone at Eaton in 1882, and the Midland Railway planned to extend their Holwell branch (recently acquired from the Holwell Iron Co) to Eaton; but it appears that the Duke of Rutland, the principal landowner, would have no truck with the Midland, and would only consent to the new line being built and worked by the Great Northern

Eaton Quarries. The trestle viaduct on the Eaton branch. In 1955 this was filled in with slag from Holwell Works. Stanton Ironworks Co Ltd

Eaton Quarries. The Eaton branch had a ruling gradient of 1 in 50; in the early days it was customary to provide two brake vans per train but later a special 8-wheeled brake van was built. This vehicle is shown here in the charge of a class 4 locomotive, 28th March 1956. J.R. Bonser

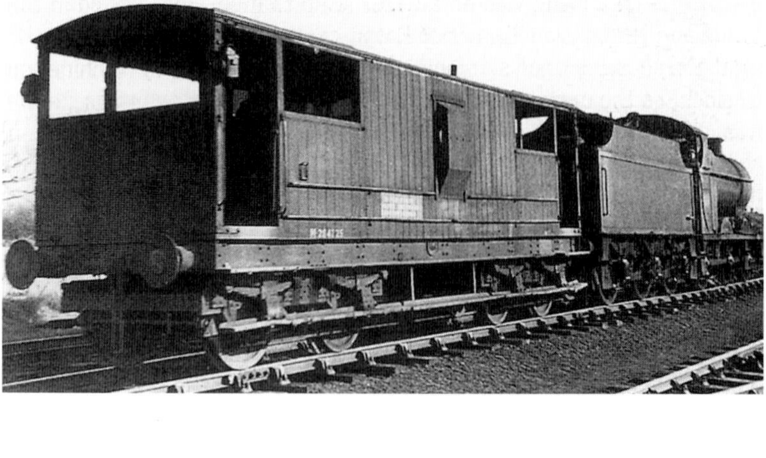

Railway. Thus came about the rather curious situation of a purely GN branch from the joint GN-LNW Railway. The Waltham-on-the-Wolds branch was opened in 1883, and the extensions to Eaton and Eastwell in 1884/85. In due course however the MR was allowed to extend its Holwell branch to meet the GNR system at Wycomb Junction, as we have already noted – this being done in 1887. An even more surprising feature of the GNR mineral system was the 'Eastwell branch', serving the Eastwell Iron Ore Co, that was already connected by incline to the Joint line. The Eaton branch was not easy to operate; it had a ruling gradient of 1 in 50, so that each loaded train had two brake vans or, in later years, a special eight-wheeled van with extra braking power. There was one curve of 8 chains radius. The most spectacular feature was the wooden trestle viaduct over a tributary of the river Devon south of Eaton village; this did not survive to the end, as in 1955 it was filled beneath with slag from Holwell works.

Most of the ore went to the quarry proprietors' own furnaces, but some was sold elsewhere. For example, when Partington Iron & Steel Co Ltd, started their works at Irlam, near Manchester, in 1912, they signed a contract with Holwell Iron Co Ltd. for the supply of ore, and this proved to be of very long standing; the ore may not have come from the Eaton quarries, but the opening of new quarries there in the period 1912-1914 may well have been influenced by this contract.

The Eaton branch at the ore-bearing end took a course roughly north to south, with quarries east and west, while many valleys on the east side ran roughly east to west, breaking up the ironstone field into 'fingers' or outliers. The operators tackled the difficult geographical conditions in their individual ways, giving the Eaton area a special charm not found elsewhere. Quarrying was on a wider scale than at Holwell and in the 1930s and 1940s the villagers of Eaton can never have been out of the sight and sound of small locomotives and the clank of quarry machines on all sides. To the narrow gauge railway enthusiast it was a paradise; there was so much to see and record. In the postwar years the situation changed with the elimination of two narrow gauge tramways – but, happily, the retention of two – the extension of two standard gauge lines and the building of a new one, and the introduction of lorry haulage. In a different way the ironstone scene was still full of interest as the remaining pockets of ironstone were dealt with.

It is hard to imagine the quiet secluded Eaton of today as the centre of a busy ironstone quarrying area, but there are well established remains and records to show that it was so.

EATON QUARRIES

Owners: Holwell Iron Co Ltd; Stanton Ironworks Co Ltd from 1st January 1918; Stewards & Lloyds Minerals Ltd. from 1st January 1950.

The quarries extended over a wide area north of the village and a smaller area to the south. To the operators they were always referred to collectively as 'Eaton Quarries', only distinguished by the titles of the working faces in the company's detailed records of output, in which transport methods were of minor importance. The number of loaded wagons sent away by rail was the important thing; whether they were filled with ore brought in by narrow gauge tramway, standard gauge tramway or lorry was immaterial. It is therefore logical to deal with the northern group of quarries as one unit in the same way as Holwell, where there existed a somewhat similar situation on a smaller scale. The southern quarries however can be segregated under the heading of Eaton Ropeway, isolated from the rest by the river Devon, and having greater geographical associations with the Eastwell system. In this section, therefore, we shall deal with the northern group of quarries, describing the different transport systems as they came into being.

Narrow gauge tramway – Duke's and Hurst's Pits

The Holwell Iron Co obtained from the Duke of Rutland leases to work ironstone in the parishes of Eaton and Waltham, both leases being dated 14th August 1882. The Waltham area was the first to be developed, in 1883, doubtless because the Great Northern Railway branch to Waltham on the Wolds was completed that year. Trial holes were made at Eaton in 1883[1]; MS first records production in 1886 but E. Wilson[2] refers to the 'Holwell Iron Co workings at Eaton' in 1885. The Waltham quarries gave disappointing results and were closed by 1885, so it is possible that the tramway equipment was transferred in that year to Eaton; there is no documentary evidence for this but it was fully in keeping with Holwell policy elsewhere.

The first workings in the Eaton district were in the vicinity of Eaton Wharf, which was a set of sidings on the west side of the Great Northern Eaton branch immediately north of the Eaton-Stathern road. The use of the word 'Wharf' will be noted here and at Holwell for a railway transhipment point instead of its more usual application to water transport. The quarrying area lay in the angle between the Eaton-

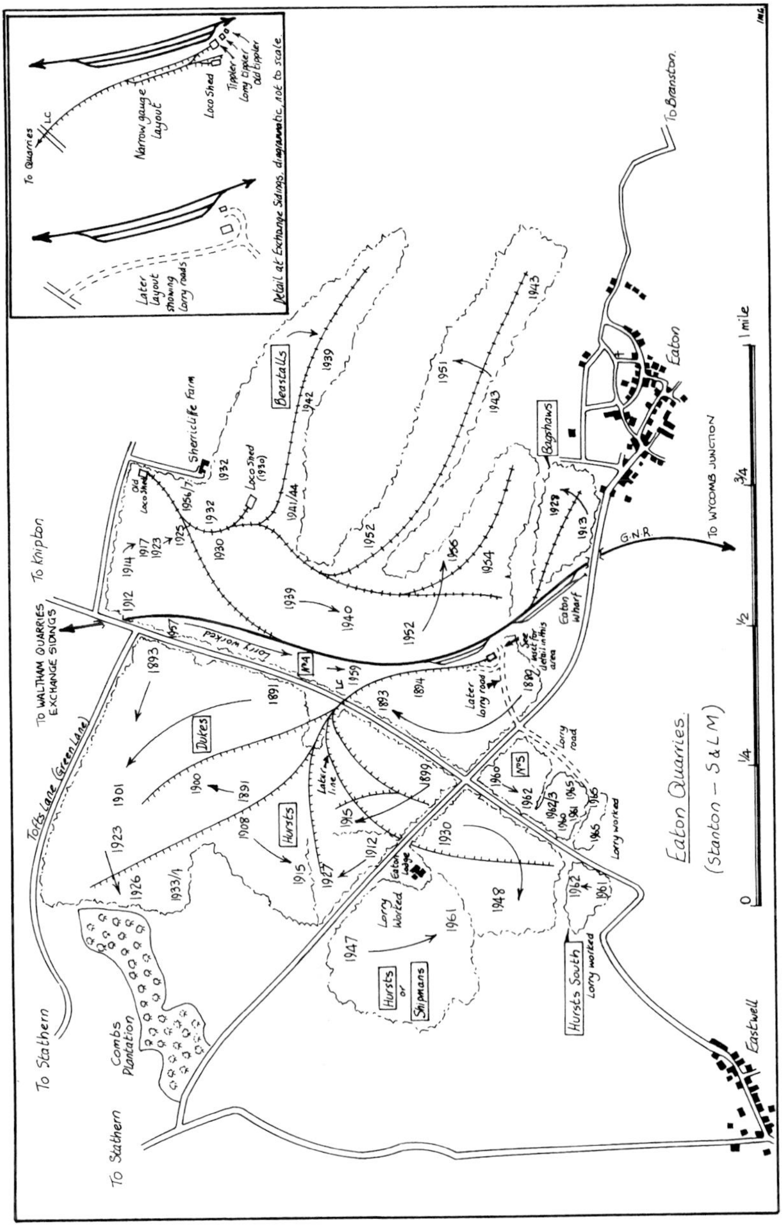
Eaton Quarries.
(Stanton – S & L M)
To Knipton
To WALTHAM QUARRIES EXCHANGE SIDINGS
Tofts Lane (Green Lane)
To Stathern
To Stathern
Combs Plantation
Eastwell
Eaton
To Branston
TO WYCOMB JUNCTION
G.N.R.
Eaton Wharf
Beastalls
Dukes
Hursts
Hursts or Shipmans
Hursts South
Lorry worked
Bagshaws
Sherricliffe Farm
Old Loco Shed
Loco Shed (1930)
Eaton Lodge
Lorry worked
Later lorry road
Lorry road
Later line
No 4
No 5
LC
Detail at Exchange Sidings, diagrammatic, not to scale.
To Quarries
Narrow gauge layout
Later layout showing lorry roads
Loco Shed
Tippler
Lorry tippler
Old tippler
0
1/4
1/2
3/4
1 mile

Stathern and Eastwell-Belvoir roads, southwards to the outcrop, and requiring only a very short tramway, for which the one used at Waltham would have been long enough; if the Waltham equipment was used, then the wagons were probably end-tippers, and horses used for haulage. The survey plans recording the annual area from which ironstone had been removed suggest that the tipping point was 200 yards north of the later tipping stage, which reinforces this suggestion, and the topography is in keeping also. In 1889 preparations were being made to open up ground west of the Eastwell-Belvoir road, and in the 'Colliery Guardian' for 8th November 1889, the company advertised for two locomotives of 3ft 1ins gauge, which suggests that the existing horse tramway was of that gauge; and Mr J. Turner of Ab Kettleby, who worked in various quarries in the district, confirms that the gauge was in fact 3ft 1ins. However, the new line was built to the 3ft gauge, using equipment transferred from Holwell quarries, and a new locomotive was purchased in 1890 from Hudswell Clarke.

The new quarry was known as the 'Duke of Rutland's Pit', generally shortened to 'Duke's Pit', and was in operation for over forty years from 1891 onwards, with breaks in production at times of reduced demand; working was mainly anticlockwise towards the outcrop and stretching as far as the green lane (Toft's Lane) beyond which lay the Waltham Ironstone Company's lease. The tramway crossed the Belvoir road on the level, with the office and a crossing-keeper's cabin alongside, and near the wharf was built a single-road locomotive shed of warm red brick and steel-framed windows. Close by was the tipping dock where the wagons were manhandled in turn on to a hand-operated plate tippler on a timber staging built over the Great Northern Railway siding; in this system the wagon was run on to a steel plate and secured by chains, the plate then being levered up to an angle sufficient to discharge the load. This was very heavy work even with a well-balanced plate, and the wagons, which came from Holwell, were only of small capacity – just under 30cwt[3]; they were side-tippers, whereas their predecessors at Eaton were probably end-tippers, as already mentioned.

The new locomotive, HOLWELL No. 6, was a 0-4-0 saddle tank of standard Hudswell Clarke design; this maker had already supplied locomotives for Stanton's 3ft line at Woolsthorpe a few miles away, and several others came in later years. This locomotive remained at Eaton until the twilight of its days, and the only other definitely known to have been here during Holwell's regime was HOLWELL No. 5, new from

Peckett's in 1912. However, the 1889 advertisement called for two locomotives and a spare would be needed when No. 6 was under repair, and the shed was built to hold two; a likely contender is the Hudswell Clarke & Rodgers known to have been at the Ropeway later. Kirkleatham ironstone mines closed in 1882, but the engine may not have come direct from them – indeed, we have no idea when she arrived, but it could have been in the 1890s. The original livery of these locomotives is not known, but in later years HOLWELL No. 6 was painted in Stanton's then standard of green, lined black edged white, and with red coupling rods and cast brass nameplates. HOLWELL No. 5 was painted in Peckett's standard light green, lined black edged yellow, with red rods and brass nameplates.

Eaton Quarries. The Peckett HOLWELL NO. 5 came here new in 1912, but later moved to Woolsthorpe, where this photograph was possibly taken. J.M.Jarvis

Returning to our description of the quarries, the next event was the extension of the potential quarrying area in 1894 by the leasing of the stone under land belonging to Mrs Hurst, to the immediate south of the Duke of Rutland's lease. Working east of the Eastwell-Belvoir road ceased in 1894, but whether it was served to the end by the old end-tipping tramway or by a branch from the new locomotive-worked line is not known. Quarrying at Hurst's pit commenced in 1898, with a branch tramway leaving the line to Duke's pit just beyond the level crossing, and working clockwise towards the outcrop, which seems to have been reached in 1915; but quarrying continued further south towards the Stathern road. From 1907 working was taken deeper to utilise the underlying more limey stone that before then was considered unsuitable for the furnaces. Quarrying in this part of Hurst's pit continued up to 1927.

In this period quarrying east of the Great Northern Railway Eaton branch commenced, with the use of standard gauge tramways, but for simplicity we will defer consideration of these until we have dealt with the area west of the railway served by the narrow gauge tramway. In January 1918 the system passed into Stanton ownership along with other Holwell properties, but operations continued much as before until the late 1920s. In 1929 a brick arch was made under the Eaton-Stathern road to open up the area on the south side, still part of the Hurst lease; here again working started from the side adjoining the Eastwell road clockwise to the initial gullet in line with the bridge, reached in 1947, then west of this towards the outcrop, working round Eaton Lodge anticlockwise from the Stathern road. Operations were then becoming more difficult because of increasing overburden; hitherto hand baring had been practised

Eaton Quarries. Caterpillar-mounted steam shovel in Hurst's pit, in September 1946, loading an early Muir-Hill dumper. BSC

throughout, even small pieces of ironstone in the few feet of overburden being forked out and tipped into the trams from the barrows used in the usual 'plank and barrow' method of removing overburden. In 1928, to deal with the boulder clay in Duke's, a long-jib steam navvy was put to work, the forerunner of general mechanisation of the Eaton quarries. The tramway was modernised also; early in 1930 the old wooden trams were replaced by steel V-tip wagons of larger capacity, and the plate tippler by a steel structure with a chute to the railway wagons below; this chute was built on a concrete base immediately north of the old plate tippler, which was dismantled.

Quarrying at Duke's pit came to an end in 1926, much the same time as in that part of Hurst's pit north of the Stathern road, but there was a short-lived revival of work near the escarpment in 1933/34. All the available stone had then been got, apart from a small area in Comb's Plantation to the south-west, which in fact was never touched. This area is collectively referred to in LI as 'Southern Terrace Hills Quarry', and stated to be 'standing' in 1939. Operations continued however in Hurst's pit south of the Stathern road (sometimes called Shipman's pit) and Eaton Lodge was left high and dry as the surrounding fields were excavated. The overburden was now heavier and the use of quarry machines general. Trials with machine loading were made in May 1936[4] and the cost of the operation were compared with a similar experiment at Glendon's Cherry Hall face; costs were found to be lower at Cherry Hall but the difference not sufficient to justify replacement of the narrow gauge rail system at Hurst's by one of standard gauge. So the little railway carried on; but quarry machinery was introduced for baring with a 43RB diesel dragline, new in 1938, and replaced by a larger machine of W80 type in 1941. A more surprising event was the transfer here in 1945 of a Ruston & Hornsby 20-ton steam navvy; she came from Glendon, doubtless moved because the work at Eaton was still in her capacity whereas this was not the case at Glendon. During the war years the accent was on continuous production, with the narrow gauge tramway using its two locomotives intensively; but afterwards, economic factors became more important, and Stanton decided to do away with its neat but outmoded surviving narrow gauge systems. Eaton was the first to go, in January 1946; the locomotives were transferred to short-lived employment elsewhere, the rails were lifted and the transport of ore was carried on by lorries, using the course of the tramway and the level crossing as a road and the locomotive shed as a garage. Tipping continued via the steel chute.

With the lorries now in charge, we will leave Hurst's quarry and take a look at the quarries east of the GNR branch; there were two standard gauge tramway systems, a relatively long-lived one to the north, usually referred to as Beastall's from the original quarry name (to distinguish the area from Duke's and Hurst's) and a much smaller and short-lived line serving Bagshaw's quarry to the south. This arrangement arose from the difficult topography of the district: west of the GNR branch the ground slopes gently and fairly evenly to the escarpment, but on the east side tributaries of the little river Devon have cut into the Marlstone to leave a pattern of alternating valleys and parallel fingers of high ground. The ironstone occurs above the 400-foot contour and the tramway layout had to be modified to suit. The Eaton branch cuts across one of these small valleys about 200 yards north of the bridge under the Eaton road, and the high ground between was the area that became Bagshaw's quarry. North of this valley is the larger area collectively known as 'Beastalls' (GSM has 'Bestalls', but 'Beastalls' is used by the operators); this extended as far as the Waltham Iron Ore Company's leases, and was worked southwards from the boundary between the two leases.

Footnotes

1. A.J. Jukes-Brown: 'Geology of the south-west part of Lincolnshire, including parts of Leicestershire and Nottinghamshire'. 1885. p.38.
2. E. Wilson: 'The Lias Marlstone of Leicestershire as a source of iron'. in 'The Midland Naturalist' 1885, p.61.
3. R.F. Perry: 'The Belvoir Iron Ore'. Transactions of the Institution of Mining Engineers, 22, 1901/02, pp. 30-34.
4. BSC East Midlands Regional Record Centre, Box 063179.

Grid References

791292	Eaton Wharf
791299	Tipping docks
789299	Level crossing
790293	Locomotive shed
785297	Bridge, Hurst's Pit
787293	Level crossing of Eaton road

Locomotives

Gauge: 3ft 0ins

HOLWELL No. 6	0-4-0ST	OC	HC	375	1890	10 x 16ins	2ft 9ins	New 12/1890	(1)
	0-4-0ST	OC	HCR	126	1872	8 x 15ins	2ft 6ins	(a)	(2)

HOLWELL No. 5	0-4-0ST	OC	P	1288	1912	10 x 15ins	2ft 6½ins	New 8/1912	(3)
STANTON No. 12	0-6-0ST	OC	HC Reb. 1/1913	429	1894	9½ x 15ins	2ft 6ins	(b)	(4)

(a) ex Walker, Maynard & Co., Kirkleatham ironstone mines, North Yorkshire; this locomotive is presumed to have been here
(b) ex Holwell ironworks 5/1925; previously at Wartnaby Quarries

(1) to Holwell ironworks 4/1943; to Waltham Quarries 10/1944. ex Waltham c 10/1944. to Tilton Quarries 1/1946
(2) to Eaton Ropeway 1914
(3) to Eaton Ropeway c 1923; ex Holwell ironworks 10/1927. to Woolsthorpe Quarries 4/1941
(4) to Woolsthorpe Quarries 1/1946

Eaton Quarries. The earliest workings in this area were in the vicinity of Eaton Wharf on the GNR branch and date from the middle 1880s. The original horse tramway was replaced by a locomotive-worked line of 3ft gauge and was extended into the 'Duke's pit' by crossing the Eastwell-Belvoir road. Our photograph shows the level crossing site on 25th March 1956, with the weigh-house still in position. By this time, lorries had taken over from the tramway.
J.R. Bonser

Eaton Quarries. Stanton introduced a standard gauge tramway to serve the area north of Eaton. Horses were used at first, but about 1925 a locomotive was obtained and a shed was built for her in a worked-out quarry near Sherricliffe farm. The photograph shows the foundations of this shed on 5th April 1953. The site has now been covered in general levelling operations.
Eric Tonks

Standard gauge tramway – Beastalls Pit

The northern extremity of Stanton's lease lay alongside the south side of the track to Sherricliffe farm that left the Eastwell-Belvoir road immediately north of the bridge over the GNR branch, following this track for a third of a mile and then the parish boundary in a generally south-eastwardly direction. The ironstone in this area was almost outcrop and operations commenced here, probably in 1911, with a standard gauge tramway making a south-facing connection with the GNR line about 300 yards south of the bridge. Output commenced in 1912 from the initial face adjacent to the GNR line, then working clockwise in an arc, as far as the parish boundary, reached in 1927. Where the workings reached the trackway just mentioned, those of the Holwell Iron Company on the south side were 3-4 feet deeper than those of the Waltham Iron Ore Co on the north side, as the latter company left the underlying limey stone in situ, while after 1907 Holwell used this stone, as at Hurst's pit. By that time the Waltham Company's land had been returned to agriculture and was not disturbed again. Horse traction was employed on the tramway; it was rather curious that the company should use steam locomotives on the narrow gauge and horses on the standard gauge, but the distance was short and the ground almost level. It was not customary to calcine in this area, and loading was directly into railway wagons at the face. As the latter swung away from the road the route for the loaded wagons to the junction became more uphill and two horses (three in wet weather) were required per 10-ton wagon. To alleviate this problem Stanton introduced steam traction in the form of a Neilson flat-topped saddle tank of advanced age, transferred from Harston; the date of its arrival is not recorded but would be before 1925, as another locomotive replaced it at Harston for working a quarry that was closed in that year. A shed was built for her at the end of the tramway, in the corner where the farm track made a right-angle bend, on ground quarried in 1926. This shed was actually in the quarry itself, a most unusual arrangement for an ironstone quarry; it was of wooden construction on concrete foundations and, when a second engine arrived in 1930, was enlarged to hold the pair. There was however little quarrying at this period because of the general slack demand. In 1930 however work started on one of the eastward extensions of the plateau north of Eaton, a spur of lan about half a mile in length and tapering to a point at its south-eastern end; this was served by a branch tramway from a junction facing the locomotive shed, and the

Eaton Quarries. The later locomotive shed serving Beastall's quarry, with locomotive ADDERLEY. Connection to BR on left; to quarries in front of the group. Mr. Yates, Area Manager, on right. c 1936. Hilda Darby

Eaton Quarries. S & L 37 almost dwarfed by the loaded hopper wagons. Photographed in the 1950s. G.L. Shipman

latter was taken down and re-erected a short way down the branch on the stub of one of the first branches to a working face. Operations on this spur of land continued to 1942, while the main tramway was extended southwards to start work on the next spur, only a small area that was worked in 1941/42; and a third spur – a longer one of threequarters of a mile this time – providing work from 1934 to 1952. The final short spur was worked from 1952 to 1956. The main tramway paralleled the BR branch and the locomotive shed was in the same position, a short way south of Sherricliffe Farm, on a short branch; gradients continued to be mainly against the load, not usual for ironstone quarries. Track was flat-bottomed, with sleepers mainly of wood but with a few of concrete.

There was the turnabout of locomotives characteristic of all Stanton's quarries, with six-wheelers predominating as the line became longer. The allocation was either one or two, with a marked tendency to regard Eaton as a sort of outpost to which the more ancient engines could be relegated; the average age of the locomotives on arrival was 51 years, and only two – IRONSTONE and ADDERLEY – dated from the 20th Century. In 1951, JASON (1902) was scheduled (per BSC archives) to come from Corby, but the latter sent 37 (1885) instead! The livery of these engines was green, lined black edged white, with red coupling rods; except for the ex-Corby 37, which was black with red rods. It is curious that this engine also was named IRONSTONE at one time, though not at Eaton. They were kept in nice condition and nameplates were brass with black backgrounds, The last two locomotives, HOLWELL No. 7 and 37, were familiarly known to the staff respectively as 'Lizzie' and 'Nellie'. Standard wagons were used, with a preference for hoppers that dwarfed the older locomotives.

Exhaustion of the southernmost spur of land north of the minor stream separating it from Bagshaw's pit was followed by brief activity at the northernmost spur in 1956/57, then rail operations ceased in September 1957, and dismantling of the tramway took place with unusual speed. The locomotives were sent away in October and the locomotive shed pulled down in November, in which month also the track was lifted, the original shed site and the quarry alongside filled in and the area returned to cultivation; by 1958 it was already hard to believe that a tramway and quarry system had ever existed. It was not however the end of quarrying; there was a long narrow strip of untouched ground between the BR branch and the Eastwell-Belvoir road, and this was worked by lorries running to the tipping dock at the terminus of the former narrow gauge system. This quarry was usually referred to as No. 4, but the same

Eaton Quarries. No 60, a Ruston steam dragline at Beastall's pit in December 1936, loading hopper wagons. The shallow overburden is noticeable. Hilda Darby

title was used in LI as applying to the face east of the railway (probably the second spur of Beastall's Pit); as LI was a contemporary account, it must be accepted, and it seems that title 'Eaton No. 4 Quarry' was merely transferred to the new lorry-worked pit. Output was recorded in the loading records as from 'Field 53', the field number quoted on the lease. Other pockets of land south-west of the crossroads were developed later – see separate section.

Grid References

791305	Road bridge over GNR branch
795305	Old locomotive shed
795302	Later locomotive shed
790302	Junction with GNR branch
800299	Old Barn face terminus
798294	Southernmost face

Locomotives

Gauge: 4ft 8½ins

STANTON No. 8	0-4-0ST	OC	N	1941	1874	12 x 20ins	3ft 6⅝ins	(a)	Scr c 1932
IRONSTONE	0-4-0ST	OC	P	1050	1907	12 x 18ins	3ft 0½ins	(b)	(1)

CURZON	0-6-0ST	IC	HE	422	1887	14 x 18ins	3ft 1ins	(c)	(2)
DARLINGTON	0-6-0ST	IC	HE	421	1887	14 x 18ins	3ft 1ins	(d)	(3)
			Reb. Wake 1915						
HOLWELL No. 3	0-4-0ST	OC	BH	266	1873	12 x 19ins	3ft 2ins	(e)	(4)
			Reb. 11/1894, 11/1901. 1/1912, 2/1935						
ADDERLEY	0-6-0ST	OC	AE	1694	1915	14½ x 20ins	3ft 5ins	(f)	(5)
37	0-4-0ST	OC	HE	344	1885	13 x 18ins	3ft 1ins	(g)	(6)
HOLWELL No. 7	0-6-0ST	IC	MW	556	1875	12 x 17ins	3ft 0ins	(h)	(7)
			Reb. HIW 1949						

(a) ex Woolsthorpe Quarries c 1924
(b) ex Glendon North Quarries 7/1930
(c) ex Market Overton Quarries 12/1932
(d) ex HIW 3/1938; prev. Glendon East Quarries
(e) ex Buckminster Quarries 3/1939
(f) ex HIW 7/1944; prev. Buckminster Quarries
(g) ex Corby steelworks 1/1951
(h) ex Market Overton Quarries 2/1954

(1) to HIW 12/1932; ex HIW 8/1933; to HIW 7/1935; ex HIW 9/1935; to HIW 3/1938; ex HIW 7/1938; to Buckminster Quarries c 1939; ex Buckminster c 1940; to HIW 8/1946
(2) to HIW 7/1931; to Buckminster Quarries 10/1933
(3) to Glendon East Quarries 9/1938
(4) to Harlaxton Quarries 9/1940
(5) to Market Overton Quarries 3/1943
(6) to Buckminster Quarries 10/1957
(7) to Woolsthorpe Quarries 10/1957

HIW – Holwell Iron Works

Standard gauge tramway – Bagshaw's Pit

This was an isolated area south-east of the Eaton branch, opposite the tipping dock serving Hurst's and Duke's quarries, and separated by a small valley from the quarrying area just described. It was opened in March 1913 for production and closed in 1928, and was served throughout by a short standard gauge tramway worked by horses, like the quarries to the north at this time. Wagons were loaded directly at the quarry face and the track was presumably flat-bottomed. There was only shallow overburden and no machines were used.

Grid Reference

791292 Junction with GNR branch

Eaton Quarries. 'Beastall's Quarry' was a general name for a series of quarries on parallel spurs of high ground stretching south-east from the Eaton branch. On these strips the ore was close to the surface. Far left can be seen a plume of steam from a locomotive near the shed and in the centre background is Sherricliffe Farm. Between them items of quarry equipment can be seen. The machine is probably the 21RB diesel dragline. April 1957. BSC

Eaton Quarries. Later workings at Eaton were served by lorries instead of tramways. One such quarry was No. 4, here being worked by the 22RB dragline/crane in April 1959. Note (left to right) the BR branch with the temporary lorry road running alongside, and the office of the former narrow gauge tramway behind the bucket cable. BSC

EATON ROPEWAY QUARRIES
Owners: Holwell Iron Co Ltd; Stanton Ironworks Co Ltd from 1st January 1918

The Holwell's company's last property in the Eaton district, though but a small one designed to work out a limited field, was perhaps the most interesting of the four from the transport point of view, and certainly the most picturesque – a delightful railway perched on the hillside and wending its way through the fields. The area to be quarried lay on Windmill Hill, a quarter mile south of Eaton village, separated from the GNR Eaton branch by the valley of the river Devon, and the main transport problem was getting the ore across the valley; possibly it was because of this difficulty that the area had not been developed earlier, as otherwise the conditions were favourable – a good quality ironstone under thin cover. When the matter was first tackled – in 1911 or possibly late 1910 – the Eastwell Iron Ore Company's negotiations to open up a large area in the vicinity of Branston were well advanced and involved the laying of a lengthy extension of their tramway from Goadby Marwood under the GN Eaton branch, over the river Devon and along the valley bottom to Branston. This line passed alongside the Holwell lease and it appears that the Holwell company were hoping to use the Eastwell tramway for conveying their ore (or some of it) to a railhead. However, Eastwell were not very happy about this arrangement and tried to 'effect an exchange of ironstone . . . to avoid having to work over our viaduct.'[1] No such exchange of leased land took place, and instead of using the Eastwell tramway, the Windmill Hill output was carried over the Devon valley by means of an aerial ropeway.

The headquarters lay in a field about 100 yards from the narrow (and then gated) lane from Eaton to Waltham on the Wolds; here was the ropeway loading station and the terminus of the three-foot line from the quarries, with a slatted wood engine shed, water tank on brick piers, coal stage, sand drier and office. The contents of the side-tipping steel wagons were shot into a steel bunker with trapdoors at the bottom from which the buckets or 'skips' of the ropeway were charged and then conveyed across the valley to Windmill Hill Siding on the Eaton branch, between Eaton Wharf and the viaduct, where they were emptied into a bunker standing over the standard gauge siding and from which railway wagons were filled as required.

Production commenced in 1914, working south from the outcrop, and an ancient Hudswell Clarke & Rodgers 0-4-0 saddle tank provided to work the tramway; the origin of this engine is uncertain, but in all probability it came from work in Duke's and Hurst's pits, displaced by their new Peckett, delivered in 1912. The aerial ropeway itself – a single cable type – proved very unsatisfactory and after numerous breakdowns it was decided to replace it by one on the bi-cable system, with one cable to carry the buckets and one to haul them. Accordingly the system was closed in 1916 and not reopened until about 1923; the new ropeway was of German design, powered by a Blaxton oil engine and had a hauling capacity of 38 tons per hour.

HOLWELL No. 5 was sent here about the time of the reopening, but in 1925 was returned to Hurst's pit, leaving the Hudswell Clarke & Rodgers in charge; the official title of the latter engine is not recorded but she went under the name of 'the Old Scrappie' and was cut up at a date unknown but believed to have been soon after the arrival of HARSTON in January 1931 from the recently closed pits at Wartnaby. The only other locomotive arrived in 1941 in the interests of increased wartime production. For most of the time the tramway was worked with one locomotive only, with no spare. The painting style of the first engine is unknown but the liveries of the other three are interesting; HOLWELL No. 5 was in Peckett's standard colours of light green lined black edged yellow, with red coupling rods, and was presumably supplied thus; while the two ex-Stanton locomotives HARSTON and STANTON No. 9 bore respectively the earlier and later Stanton liveries. The former was red-brown lined black and the latter green lined black edged with white, and both had red rods. Wooden wagons similar to those at Scaldwell were used in earlier years but were later replaced by V-shaped steel side-tippers of the type supplied to work Hurst's pit, and probably at the same time, 1930. A number of the wooden wagons lay derelict in a siding by the ropeway almost to the end.

The quarrying area was restricted and the tramway only about half a mile in length. Ground north of the tramway, which was on the outcrop on the south side of the Devon valley, was worked first, then south of the main tramway, in two pits; the western face, known as Windmill Hill quarry, was worked anti-clockwise from south-south-west towards the south east, while the eastern face, known as Hubbards quarry, was worked clockwise, and in 1940 LI reports that the two faces were almost parallel, but that only Hubbards was working. In that year the tramway was extended up a minor valley to the outskirts of Eaton Grange and Mill

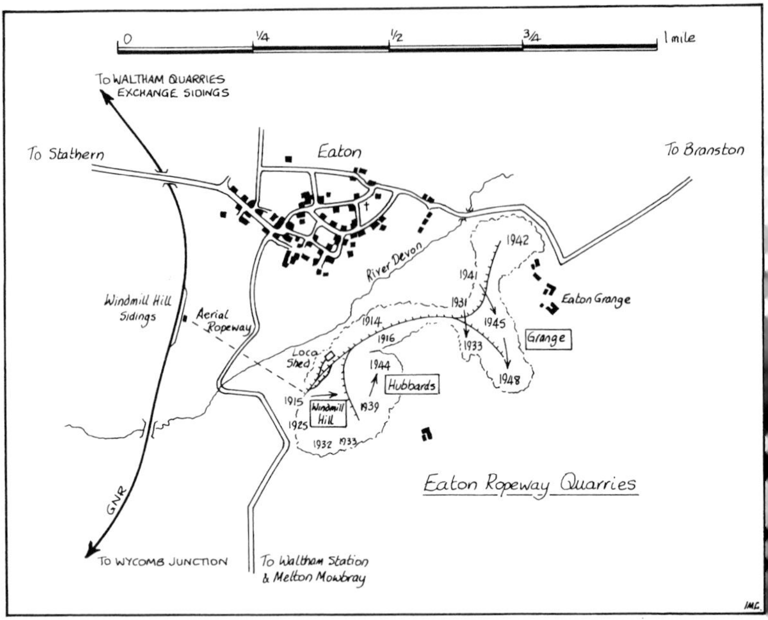

Eaton Ropeway Quarries. The only known photograph of the ropeway, taken from the embankment of the Eaton branch and showing the unloading station with chutes for filling railway wagons. Pylons and buckets of the ropeway can be seen at the rear. RRM Archives

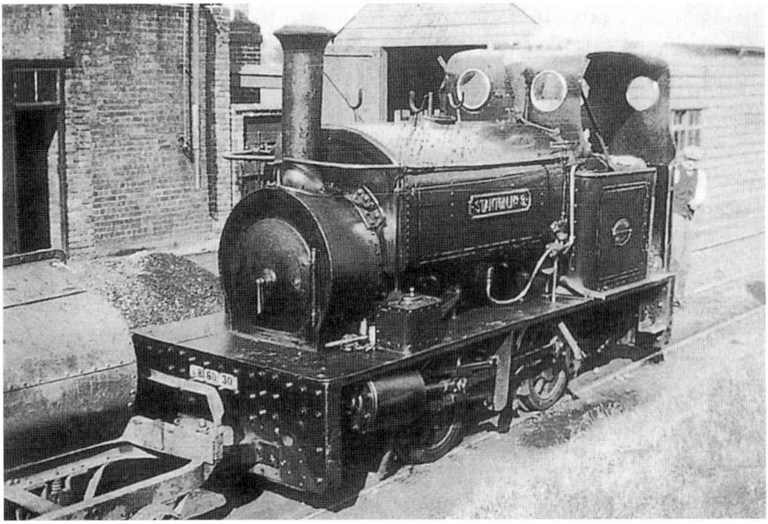

Eaton Ropeway Quarries. STANTON No. 9 with side-tipping wagons near the terminus. Behind the locomotive is the engine shed, and to the left the water tank. October 1944.

Eric Tonks

Eaton Ropeway Quarries. Stanton's remaining 3ft gauge ironstone tramways were swept away in the post-war years, and our picture shows a typical scene of desolation. Cutting up of STANTON No. 9 has begun and HARSTON awaits its fate. Discarded wagons lie by the bank and soon this enchanting spot would disappear for ever. 25th July 1949.

K. Cooper/IRS Collection

Hill House, where quarrying continued up to 1948, right up to the boundaries of the two estates – this being Grange quarry. Hubbards quarry was also reopened and worked to 1944. The main tramway then extended almost as far as the Eastwell Iron Ore Company's line and its closure was already being considered as a matter of policy when the question was settled by the breakage of the cable in about May 1948; tramway traffic then ceased and the remainder of the stone was removed by lorries to the tipping dock of the former narrow gauge tramway at Eaton Wharf, already given over to road transport. Three Dennis lorries commenced work in September 1948, and completed the removal of the stone on Windmill Hill in about three years. The tramway and ropeway were dismantled in the summer of 1949.

The overburden was generally very small, the earthworks of the tramway light, the buildings simple, and most traces soon disappeared. Indeed, of the tramway itself it may be said that nothing remains; the brickwork of the water tower was left standing for some years (it was still there in 1964) but was later demolished and only a section of brickwork and doorway was left in 1986. The quarry area has been restored to cultivation, crossed by replacement hedges, and the bridleway from Eaton Grange to the Waltham road has a marked dip at the edge of quarrying in line with a very well preserved terminal face along two sides of the grounds of Mill Hill House, visible from the Branston road and providing the most prominent reminder of quarrying in Eaton.

Footnote

1. Staveley Coal & Iron Co Ltd. – board minutes, 30th May 1911.

Grid References

793287	Discharging point on GNR branch
796286	Locomotive shed
803290	Terminus by Eaton Grange

Locomotives

Gauge: 3ft 0ins

–	0-4-0ST	OC	HCR	126	1872	8 x 15ins	2ft 6ins	(a)	Scr c 1931
HOLWELL No. 5	0-4-0ST	OC	P	1288	1912	10 x 15ins	2ft 6½ins	(b)	(1)
HARSTON	0-4-0ST	OC	WB	1587	1900	9 x 14ins	2ft 3½ins	(c)	Scr 9/1949
STANTON No. 9	0-4-0ST	OC	HC	506	1898	9 x 15ins	2ft 3ins	(d)	Scr 7/1949
			Reb. Wake 1916						

(a) ex Eaton Quarries 1914
(b) ex Eaton Quarries c 1923
(c) ex Wartnaby Quarries 1/1931
(d) ex Tilton Quarries 4/1941 (could be HC 505 (same dimensions; history ambiguous)

(1) to Holwell Ironworks 5/1925; to Eaton Quarries 10/1927

Quarry Machines
(Collective list – Narrow gauge tramways: Standard gauge tramways; lorry-worked quarries)

No. 20	S. Dragline. Long Jib	RH 1273	1928	1¼ Cu. Yds.	60ft.	New 5/1928	(1)
No. 8	S. Navvy	RP 346	1912	½ Cu. Yd.	25ft.	(a)	(2)
No. 60	S. Dragline. Caterpillar	RH 795	1923	1½ Cu. Yds.	60ft.	(b)	(3)
21RB	D. Dragline	RB 3306	1937	⅜ Cu. Yds.	50ft.	(c)	(4)
422	D. Dragline	R&R 619	1937	½ Cu. Yd.	35ft.	(d)	(5)
43RB	D. Dragline. Long Jib. Crawler	RB 3856	1938	¾ Cu. Yd.	70ft.	New 5/1938	(6)
W 80 No. 246	D. Walking Dragline	R&R 1031	1939	2 Cu. Yds.	90ft.	New 11/1939(e)	(7)
33RB	D. Dragline	RB 6474	1942	1½ Cu. Yds.	45ft.	New 7/1942	(8)
No. 20	S. Shovel (f. Dragline.) Caterpillar	RH 1183	1927	1 Cu. Yd.	52ft.	(f)	(9)
S 34	D. Dragline	Lima 4383	1947				s/s
S 34	D. Dragline	Lima 4384	1947	¾ Cu. Yd.	50ft.	(g)	(10)
55RB	E. Crane. Crawler	RB 4975	1940	2 Cu. yds.	60ft.	(h)	(11)
22RB	D. Dragline/Crane	RB 21136	1956	¾ Cu. Yd.	40ft.	New 9/1956	(12)
10RB	D. Dragline	RB 18290	1954	10 Cu. Ft.	35ft.	(i)	(13)
24RB	D. Dragline	RB 4951	1940	½ Cu. Yd.	60ft.	(j)	(14)

(a) ex H. Potter & Co, 2/1929
(b) ex F. Edmunds, dealer, 10/1933; prev. Riverlands Improvement Board, Derby
(c) ex Stanton Spun Pipe Plant, 7/1937
(d) ex Stanton Spun Pipe Plant, 11/1937
(e) New 11/1939 per R&R records; Stanton records give 3/1941
(f) ex Glendon North Quarries 5/1945
(g) ex Buckminster Quarries 4/1948
(h) ex Woolsthorpe Quarries 11/1949
(i) ex Harlaxton Quarries 5/1961
(j) ex Eastwell Quarries c 1967

(1) at Duke's pit throughout. To Glendon Quarries 11/1936
(2) to Market Overton Quarries 1/1936
(3) New boiler fitted at RB 7-9/1936. At Beastall's pit, 1936-39. To Thos W. Ward Ltd. 1951
(4) at Beastall's pit 1937. To Woolsthorpe Quarries 8/1940; ex Glendon Quarries 1/1942; to Buckminster Quarries 1/1943; ex Harlaxton Quarries 3/1945. To Tilton Quarries 6/1952

(5) To Woolsthorpe Quarries 6/1947
(6) New to Hurst's pit 1938. To Tilton Quarries 4/1941
(7) at Hurst's pit. To Stanton ironworks c 1963; ex Stanton 1/1965. At Eaton No. 4 qy. To Ferguson Plant, Scunthorpe, c 1968
(8) at Hurst's pit; at Beastall's Old Barn face 1957. To A. R. Clay, dealer, 5/1964
(9) at Hurst's pit, s/s
(10) To Pen Green shops, Corby 9/1952
(11) To Market Overton Quarries 9/1951
(12) at Hurst's pit 1959; at No. 4 quarry 1959; to Buckminster Quarries
(13) To Woolsthorpe Quarries c 1962
(14) at Eastwell No. 5, Basic and Mill Hill quarries, on restoration. To Warsop Sand Quarries (?) c 1973

EATON BASIC QUARRIES
Owners: Basic Ironstone Co; Park Gate Iron & Steel Co Ltd from c.1921

The curiously-named Basic quarries occupied only a small area but the history of its exploitation is extraordinarily complex, partly because of geographical difficulties and partly because of the interplay of interests by different operators. The story begins in 1913, when the Duke of Rutland offered to Staveley Coal & Iron Co Ltd the lease of 120 acres of land adjoining the Branston lease recently acquired from the Duke; the ironstone, being limey, carried the lower royalty of 3d per ton against the 7½d charged on the general run of outcrop Eaton ore. Park Gate Iron & Steel Co Ltd. were interested, and Staveley proposed that the Eastwell Iron Ore Co take over the lease and sell the ore to Park Gate. However, James Oakes (one of Staveley's co-partners in the Eastwell Iron Ore Co) was not in favour of this and as a result Staveley obtained the lease in their own right and then transferred it to Park Gate; Staveley had a managing interest in all Park Gate's ironstone activities in the East Midlands. The siding agreement of 6th August 1915 was between the GNR and Staveley Coal & Iron Co Ltd, and on 1st July 1948 this was transferred to Staveley Iron & Chemical Co Ltd. Initially the quarries were operated by a nominally independent company, The Basic Ironstone Co, in true Staveley fashion, but soon came under Park Gate.

The area involved lay west of the Eaton branch immediately north of the viaduct, and a standard gauge tramway was laid to the outcrop on the north side of the Devon tributary from a junction facing the branch terminus. This short line was, like the one to Holwell's Bagshaw quarry, worked by horses; production commenced in 1916 and ceased about 1932. In 1927 began the construction of a tramway to a quarry half a mile to the north-west, where the ironstone was under a heavier overburden. This tramway left the LNER siding in the opposite direction and was taken in a sharp curve through a deep cutting, the spoil from which was carried overland on a two-foot gauge tramway and used to fill in the earlier workings. Motive power on this line was the little Bagnall PIXIE, which was used on similar work at Pilton and Pitsford. PIXIE was a Staveley engine and came here under the pooled arrangements for quarry management between Staveley and Park Gate. Five V-shaped steel side-tipping wagons, painted black, lay for many years (they were still there in 1964) outside the locomotive shed, and presumably once worked on the overland line. A small petrol-driven navvy was used to dig out the spoil.

The later quarry line had the distinction amongst standard gauge ironstone systems of having been worked solely by internal-combustion locomotives, the short haul being more economically worked by them than by steam. There were two locomotives, the first built by Howards of Bedford for the War Department, Weedon, and fitted with a 40hp Dorman engine; she is believed to be the last of her type in use in this country, when in 1949 she was superseded by a Fowler diesel locomotive. This had a 52 hp Ruston engine and as received from Park Gate ironworks was painted black; she was soon repainted dark green but in the Spring of 1961 appeared in a livery of light green with dark green shutters for the engine bonnet, red rods, and the legend PARK GATE IRON & STEEL CO LTD in white paint along the top of the right hand side of the bonnet; she had cast-iron nameplates DOUGLAS, with white letters on a black background. The loco was housed in a small wooden shed, similar in design to that at Park Gate's Sproxton quarry, but this one – never having had to contain a steam locomotive – lacked the familiar 'pot' and looked even more like a garden shed. Except in the quarry, the track was chaired, an unusual refinement for so short a line.

The output went via the former Great Northern line to Scalford Junction, at a time when that from other quarries on the Eaton branch went via the former Midland Railway route. When the overburden became heavier – 20 feet or more – an excavator was introduced to deal with it; this was a steam navvy crane, rather surprising in view of the non-steam locomotive side. She was a dual-purpose machine, and could be fitted with a long jib and bucket for digging out the stone, or as a dragline for removing overburden. According to Staveley files, she was a 20-ton machine, No. 496, which RP records quote as 8-ton.

The high ground on each side of the tramway cutting between loco shed and the BR branch was part of the Park Gate lease, but as the overburden removal was beyond the capacity of their steam navvy, this area was not tackled by them, but with bigger machines by Staveley Minerals Ltd after the latter had completed their Mill Hill operations on the east side of the BR line; as well as quarry equipment and locomotive, they brought with them the title 'Mill HIll' also, and for a short period both operators were working almost alongside each other. To the casual observer it must have appeared as a mere continuation of Park Gate's activities – and to some extent it was, as Staveley had always managed Park Gate's ironstone properties. To add to the complications, Stewarts

Eaton Basic Quarries. This was one of the very few ironstone quarries to be worked by internal-combustion locomotives from early days. DOUGLAS, JF 21086, stands outside the engine shed (note that it has no 'pots') on 20th April 1960. Road to Eaton village behind shed. S.A. Leleux

Eaton Basic Quarries. While the locomotive was diesel, the quarry machine was a dual-purpose Ruston steamer, which could be used with a dragline and bucket (as here) or with a shovel. 5th April 1953. Eric Tonks

& Lloyds Minerals Ltd. had from 1960 been working by lorry the field to the north of the Basic quarry, between it and the Eastwell-Belvoir road. Staveley Minerals Ltd (in their own right and not as manager for Park Gate) commenced operations in July 1961 at a small pocket of ore alongside the BR branch close to the Eaton road, thus not interfering with Park Gate's operations. The Basic quarry was closed 2nd September 1961 and Staveley then took over the tramway between the BR junction and locomotive shed, and started work much further south, from where Park Gate had left off in 1932. These operations were officially regarded as Mill Hill and are described under that heading.

Park Gate's *quarry* track was disused and the steam navvy sent to Renishaw ironworks as a crane; the diesel locomotive was not used by Staveley, but remained in the shed throughout Staveley's occupation of the site. The remaining former Basic track was still in position in the summer of 1963 but was lifted in the following year, when also the railway cutting blasted through the rock to the Eaton branch was filled in (see Mill Hill notes). In the winter of 1967/68 the locomotives shed was demolished and the main quarrying area levelled, along with the adjacent Mill Hill site and No. 5 Quarry.

Grid References

792286	Original junction with GNR branch, by viaduct
792290	Later junction with BR branch, by road
789291	Locomotive shed
790291	Deep cutting, north end

Locomotives

Gauge: 4ft 8½ins

–	4WPM	H	950	1929	40hp	7 tons	(a)	(1)
DOUGLAS	0-4-0DM	JF	21086	1936	52hp		(b)	(2)

(a) ex War Department, Weedon, Northamptonshire
(b) ex Park Gate Ironworks, 8/1949

(1) to Staveley Iron & Chemical Co Ltd, Warsop Sand Quarries, Nottinghamshire, 1949
(2) to Mill Hill Quarries 9/1961

Gauge: 2ft 0ins

PIXIE	0-4-0ST	OC	WB 2090	1919	6 x 9ins	1ft 7ins	(a)	(1)

(a) ex Pilton Ironstone Co, 1928

(1) to Pitsford Ironstone Co, c 1933

Quarry Machines

No. 8	S. Shovel/Dragline	RP 496	1917	1½ Cu. Yds.	25ft.	(a)	(1)
43RB	D. Shovel	RB 3799	1938	1¾ Cu. Yds.	27ft.	(b)	s/s c 1966
43RB	D. Shovel	RB 6747	1942	1¾ Cu. Yds.	22ft.	(c)	s/s c 1967

(a) ex Lamport Quarries 1942 (see text for comment)
(b) ex Eastwell Quarries c 1965
(c) ex Lamport Quarries 1965. This machine may possibly have been at Mill Hill.

(1) to Renishaw Ironworks, Derbyshire, 1/1962

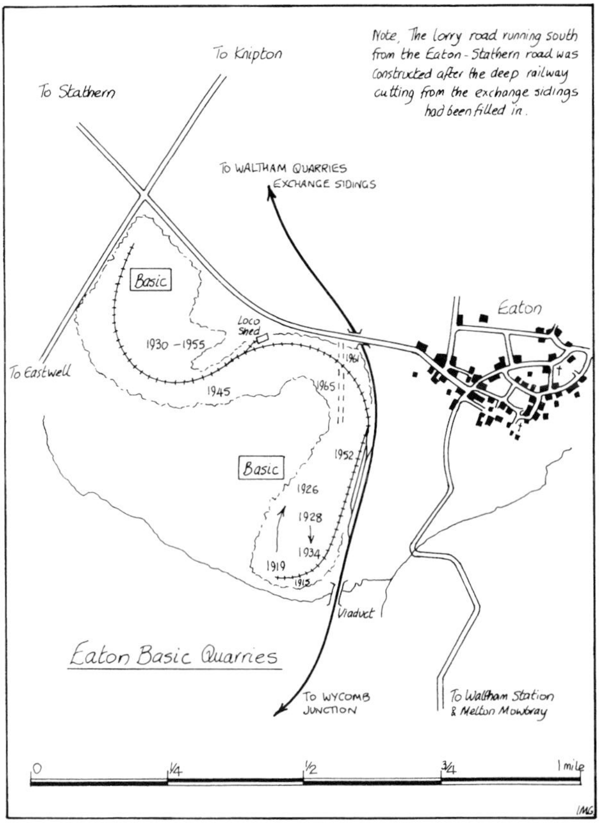

MILL HILL QUARRIES

Owners: Eastwell & Waltham Ironstone Co Ltd; Eastwell & Loddington Ironstone Co Ltd from 23rd October 1959; Staveley Minerals Ltd from 7th March 1961.

This was the last entirely separate ironstone quarry system in the Midlands, which is rather surprising in view of the continuous and intensive working in the Eaton district for threequarters of a century, and was due to its being a small area of ironstone under cover thicker than usual for Eaton. The site lay on the south-west side of the Eaton-Stathern road on the rising ground through which passed the BR Eaton branch. Preparation of the area east of the railway commenced in 1956, and in July 1957 the BR siding that had formerly served the ropeway, and which had been out of use since the breakdown of the latter in 1948, was extended into the quarrying area. As the Ropeway quarries were on Windmill Hill, this siding was called Windmill Hill Siding, and the new quarry was therefore officially known as Mill Hill quarry – though in fact the workings were not on Windmill Hill, but on ground separated from it by the valley of the Devon; the same valley separated the working area from the 3ft gauge tramway of the Eastwell & Waltham Ironstone Co, the owners of the Mill Hill site.

To work the new standard gauge line a large six-coupled Peckett locomotive was obtained second-hand and repainted light green with red rods, at the end of the BR Eaton branch by the Eastwell & Waltham Ironstone Company's premises; she was sent to Mill Hill in July 1957. A locomotive shed of red corrugated iron with green window frames was built in the autumn of 1957 at the BR end of the new line, adjacent to the Eaton branch. The tramway was short but the load had to be taken uphill, hence the six-wheeler; about 1958 a second-hand diesel was considered, but it was realised that nothing less than 200 hp would suffice, and there were no such locomotives available.

Two 54RB machines were obtained new for stripping and loading, and the area was exhausted in just under four years, quarrying ceasing about the end of May 1961; the entire equipment was then moved west of the railway to open up ground there, still as 'Mill Hill Quarries' officially, though now removed a stage further away; this area adjoined the Basic quarries, and, as described under that heading, use was made of their tramway, which was still dealing with output from Basic up to the closure on 2nd September 1961. Mill Hill's Peckett was moved to the west site in

Mill Hill Quarry. We refer readers to the text for the discussion on the involved history of operations here. The photograph shows the rail connections on 27th April 1960, with the BA Eaton branch in the centre, line to Mill Hill quarry left, and to Basic quarry, right.

D.H. Newman

Mill Hill Quarries. P 1952 rests in the dappled shade from the trees across the BR branch. A shed was later built for her on this spot. Road to Eaton village at top. 1957

P.D. Rowbotham

July 1961 and for the first two months dealt with a small pocket of ore close to the road, thus not interfering with Park Gate's operations. From 1st September 1961 however work commenced on the first strip of the main area, taking over from where Park Gate had abandoned their southern workings in 1932. Demolition of the old Mill Hill locomotive shed commenced in May 1961 but was then held up until September, when the materials could be used to raise and extend the Park Gate shed to accommodate the Peckett as well as DOUGLAS. Quarrying ceased on the east side about the end of May, and by the end of 1961 the old Mill Hill site had been restored to cultivation, the only evidence apart from the lowered field level being the stub of the point from the BR line.

Rail operation continued on the west side for two years, but in the summer of 1963 preparations were made to introduce lorry haulage by laying a special road from the quarry to the Eaton road, across the tramway cutting near the footbridge. The cutting was filled in at this point, leaving the diesel (which had lain disused since the closure of the Basic quarry) isolated in the shed, and the Peckett standing on the spur, ready to work the traffic until the lorry road was completed, which took place at the end of the summer. The Peckett (it never had a title) was laid aside and taken away for scrap at the beginning of December. By July 1964 all track had been lifted, leaving the lorries in complete charge.

Grid References

793291	Locomotive shed
794287	Terminus, south east end

Locomotives

East Site
Gauge: 4ft 8½ins

–	0-6-0ST	OC	P	1952	1938	16 x 24ins	3ft 10ins	(a)	(1)

(a) ex Tyne Improvement Commissioners 10/1956, per Abelson & Co (Engineers) Ltd, Sheldon, Birmingham: to Waltham Quarries for repair; to Mill Hill site 7/1957

(1) to West Site 7/1961.

West Site
Gauge: 4ft 8½ins

–	0-6-0ST	OC	P	1952	1938	16 x 24ins	3ft 10ins	(a)	(1)
DOUGLAS	0-4-0DM		JF	21086	1936	52hp		(b)	(2)

(a) ex East Site 7/1961
(b) ex Basic Quarries 9/1961

(1) to A. E. Burgess & Sons Ltd, Belgrave Road station, Leicester 12/1963; scr 12/1963
(2) to Lamport Sidings, Northamptonshire 12/1965

Quarry machines

54RB	D. Dragline	RB 22150	1957			New 6/1957	(1)
54RB	D. Dragline	RB 24553	1960	2 Cu. yds.	70ft.	New 9/1960	(2)

(1) to Harlaxton Quarries c 1961
(2) to Sproxton Quarries c 1961

See note under Eaton Basic Quarries.

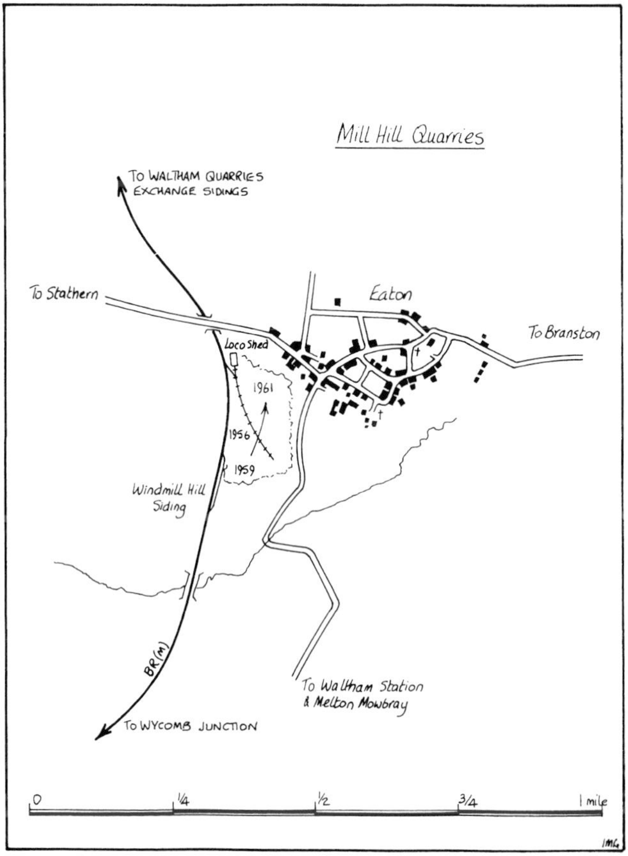

THE LORRY WORKINGS AT EATON

The introduction of lorries emphasised that to the operator 'Eaton Quarries' embraced all the quarries served by different tramways, and with the passage of time it became difficult to consider the new workings solely in relation to the former tramways; we have therefore grouped them under the above heading and will now look at the individual quarries in the order in which they were opened up.

1. Hurst's Quarry (formerly served by narrow gauge tramway) Owners: Stanton Ironworks Co Ltd; Stewarts & Lloyds Minerals Ltd from 1st January 1950 .

Operations commenced immediately north-west of Eaton Lodge early in 1946 (the tramway being closed in January) and the output was conveyed by Muir Hill dumpers along the route of the former narrow gauge tramway to the same tipping dock, where the chute was modified to accept the larger loads discharged. Three Dennis lorries with tip-up backs were purchased in the autumn of 1947 and two were housed in the locomotive shed, which was lengthened by means of a green corrugated iron extension in the front. In 1956 AEC 'Monarch' lorries, transferred from Woolsthorpe, were used. The steam navvy was used at first, and later machines included 22RB, 33RB and a W80 walking dragline. Work continued in a generally anti-clockwise direction from Eaton Lodge, up to May 1961, making this quarry the one with the longest history of lorry operation in the Midlands. Operations were then continued at Eaton No. 5 Quarry and Hurst's Face South (see below).

2. Windmill Hill Quarry (formerly served by narrow gauge tramway) Owners: Stanton Ironworks Co Ltd; Stewarts & Lloyds Minerals Ltd from 1st January 1950.

Tramway operation ceased in May 1948, as already described, and three five-ton Dennis lorries commenced work in September 1948; they had been purchased in 1947 and are presumed to have been used at Hurst's face first. There may well have been some pooling arrangement, as the lorries used the same tipping dock by Eaton Wharf. The date of completion of the work at Windmill Hill is not recorded, but is believed to have been in 1951; certainly there was only a small quantity of stone to be removed. It seems likely that a small machine would be required for loading – presumably one of those recorded in the Eaton list, but specific details have not survived.

3. Eaton No. 4 Quarry (new quarry)
Owners: Stewarts & Lloyds Minerals Ltd.

The standard gauge tramway served 'Eaton No. 4 quarry' at an early date, but this face disappeared as southward extensions to Beastall's Quarry were made; to latter-day personnel Eaton no. 4 was the title applied to the narrow strip of land between the Eaton branch and the Eastwell-Belvoir road, and as such bore no connection other than title with the 'Eaton No. 4' mentioned in LI. In BSC records it is referred to as 'Field 53'.

Eaton Quarries. A contrast in early lorry operation. In the foreground an AEC Dumptruck, at the rear an earlier AEC 'Monarch' tipping lorry. October 1960, probably at Eaton No 5 quarry.
BSC

Operations commenced in 1957 with AEC 'dump trucks,' more sophisticated machines than the early tip-up lorries, and combining the manoeuvrability of a dumper with the loading of a lorry. The output was carried to the Eaton Wharf tipping dock along a special road bed alongside the BR line. In the 1956-57 correspondence files in BSC archives, there is mention of new tipping dock to segregate the softer, siliceous stone of No. 4 quarry from the more limey stone of Hurst's, possibly in the form of a separate chute at the Wharf; but it seems doubtful whether this was implemented, as the personnel at Sysonby Lodge have no recollection of it. The reference to the tipping dock being brought into use in July 1957 probably refers to the commencement of operations from No. 4 quarry, at a time when Hurst's was not working. There was not a great deal of ground to be tackled at No. 4, and the work was completed about October 1959.

4. Eaton No. 5 Quarry (new quarry)
Owners: Stewarts & Lloyds Minerals Ltd; Staveley Minerals Ltd from June 1963.

There is no uncertainty about the number of this quarry, which was the last face to be opened at the crossing of the Eaton-Stathern and Eastwell-Belvoir roads, and consisted of a single large field alongside the former road, lying between it and Park Gate's Basic quarry. Operations commenced in October 1960, probably using dumptrucks transferred from No. 4 quarry. A new lorry road was built to give direct access to the Eaton Wharf tipping dock, crossing the Eaton road below the crossroads. Two faces were developed, known as No. 5 (siliceous stone) and No. 5A (limey stone; this site adjoined the old Basic Quarry, which was also a limey stone, as its name implies); but before the area had been exhausted, operations were transferred to Staveley Minerals Ltd in June 1963. They continued to work the same faces but the quarry was called Eastwell No. 5, as Staveley Minerals Ltd here was formerly Eastwell & Loddington Ironstone Co Ltd. Another change was that the lorries worked to Eastwell's tipping dock at Stathern Ironstone Sidings instead of at Eaton Wharf. It is reported that a 'mixed bag' of lorries worked here, including Scammells; and towards the end of operations a W80 Walking Dragline was moved here. Quarrying continued up to December 1965, leaving a small central area untouched.

Eaton Quarries. The loading stage at Eaton Wharf, with an AEC lorry discharging its load into the chute. To the left of the rail and ladder can be seen the site of the original plate tippler of narrow gauge tramway days. An interesting variety of hopper wagons are on display. 2nd November 1953. BSC

5. Hurst's South Quarry (new quarry)
Owners: Stewarts & Lloyds Minerals Ltd

This was no more than an extension southwards of Hurst's Pit, in the angle where the Eastwell road makes a swastika-like bend to cross a stream. Operations commenced about May 1961, using A.E.C. 'Monarch' lorries, as at Hurst's main quarry; the lorries reached the Eastwell road via a gate and travelled to Eaton Wharf dock. Operations continued up to September 1962.

6. Mill Hill Quarry (formerly worked by standard gauge tramway)
Owners: Staveley Minerals Ltd

This was the last of the Eaton faces to be worked by lorry, commencing in September 1963, only three months after Staveley had taken over from Stewarts & Lloyds Minerals Ltd the working of No. 5 quarry, a half mile to the west; the Mill Hill and No. 5 quarries lay respectively east and west of the former Basic Quarry. A separate lorry road was made to the Eaton road, crossing over the course of the very deep tramway cutting, which was filled in at this point; and the lorries or dump trucks ran to Stathern tipping dock. Operations came to an end in December 1965, the same time as at Eastwell No. 5. In the winter of 1967/68 the quarrying area embracing Basic, No. 5 and Mill Hill was levelled by two draglines.

The lorry workings at Eaton have left few traces other than sunken fields indistinguishable from those appertaining to tramway working, and the lorry roads. At Hurst's the lorries used the former tramway route: Eaton No. 5, Eaton No. 4 and Mill Hill had special roads laid for them. The rest used public roads almost entirely. There were no special garages for the lorries (as was the case elsewhere generally); the 'garage' serving Hurst's pit was the old locomotive shed and belongs to that era.

Grid References

787293	Egress of lorry road to Wharf
783291	Egress of lorry road at Hurst's No. 5
792292	Egress of lorry road from Mill HIll North (over old cutting site)
795291	No. 5 Face, south end
791293	Tipping dock

EATON AFTER RESTORATION

These notes relate to the contiguous quarrying areas to the immediate north of Eaton formerly worked by Stewarts & Lloyds Minerals Ltd (Eaton), Staveley Minerals Ltd (Mill Hill) and Park Gate Iron & Steel Co Ltd (Basic) and their predecessors. The interested observer of these quarries in their working days would visit and note them all as a matter of course and the same applies to the industrial archaeologist of today looking for traces of bygone activity.

The best starting point is the railway bridge west of Eaton on the Stathern road; the course of the BR (formerly Great Northern) Eaton branch is readily traceable for most of its distance, and northwards from this bridge can be seen the cutting and Eaton Wharf and the road access to the latter. Southwards is a complete contrast, with the whole area landscaped to give a smooth slope where once were the railway cutting and the site of Mill Hill quarries on each side. Beyond the large new field however the course of the railway is as it was left after the lifting of rails. Of the east Mill Hill site nothing recognisable remains – just one sunken field stretching to the narrow lane to Waltham, and a wire fence; the west side is similarly undistinguished except for the course of the lorry road leading over the hill from an iron gate. Of the Basic quarries one can see where they began and where they ended; at their first site on the southern flank of the hill the course of the tramway can vaguely be made out and some irregularities of the ground associated with the quarrying. There is no trace whatever of the later tramway, but there is the terminal face at the western extent of the lease, running at right angles to the Eaton-Stathern road. At the top of this face is the boundary hedge, and on the other side is No. 5 quarry, also fully restored; but there is no final face here, and the depth of working seems to be less – but that may be due to the restoration. A small triangle of unworked land shows as a piece of higher ground, and at one point the boundary with the Basic quarry has been quarried away, and the hedge – giving way to a wooden fence here – follows the contours. Part of the concrete lorry road remains, running to and across the Eaton road to the tipping dock; the double gates to the Eaton road are of wood, and the lorry road is now (1988) becoming moss grown, but still easy to follow and taking us to the most interesting set of exhibits that Eaton has to offer, at the headquarters of the narrow gauge tramway.

First, there is the locomotive shed, now used to house farm implements but easily recognisable for what it was. The original structure is of red brick with four iron-framed windows and corrugated iron sheeting in the roof where once were the two 'pots' over the loco chimneys; and an extension on the front, of green corrugated iron, to shelter the larger lorries – the concrete floor here has no provision for narrow gauge track. The lorry routes to the tipping dock are clear and so is the dock itself. This includes the site of the plate tippler, with a pair of rails sticking out from the platform of decaying planks, and the concrete base for the later iron chute. The high retaining wall alongside the railway is intact. The fields surrounding this area are below ground level. The former rail and lorry route to the level crossing is clearly defined, and the office in its grove of trees by the crossing is still there; but beyond the gates there are no traces other than sunken ground. The bridge under the Eaton-Stathern road has been filled with rubble, soiled over and grassed, and the parapets removed – restored in fact better than the flanking quarry walls below the road! Eaton Lodge stands well above ground level. At Hurst's South pit it is only possible to infer quarrying from the wire fence and from the wooden gates where lorries reached the Eastwell road.

The Great Northern Railway Eaton branch is still very well defined but from it one looks entirely in vain for traces of the quarrying activities of 'Beastalls'. Even when the place was working, the locomotive shed was very difficult of access, calling for a zigzag approach by rail or an equally lengthy walk via Sherricliffe Farm or by field path from Eaton; it was literally in the middle of fields. The bridleway past Sherricliffe Farm is now part of a long-distance footpath (the Jubilee Way, opened in 1977), indicated by the standard orb-and-crown markings on posts; as we leave the Belvoir road, it will be noted that the ground on the south side has been quarried away fairly deeply, and to the north only shallowly – the former being by Holwell Iron Co Ltd, the latter by Waltham Ironstone Co. The explanation for this has already been given. The bridleway makes a right angle turn and in the angle was the original locomotive shed, the foundations of which are now buried. Pressing on past the farm and over a field, we reach a stile and an area of open ground, with the edge of the worked spur of ground clearly visible. The later locomotive shed was near this stile, but it takes the eye of faith to believe this. In early days the only access to the shed was via the footpath to Eaton village, or along the rails; and what a lovely spot to see a locomotive shimmering in the sun! As we near the village the path crosses another dip in the ground, and to the west can be seen the site of the terminal face of Bagshaw's quarry.

Eaton Quarries. A party of IRS members explored the Eaton area on 15th October 1988 and are here shown grouped round the former narrow gauge locomotive shed at Eaton Wharf.
A.J. Cocklin

While the Eaton quarries, all within sight or sound of the village, were in the control of Holwell Iron Co, there were two other equally interesting and important quarry systems on the perimeter, both controlled by Staveley, and greatly adding to the interest, particularly among narrow gauge railway enthusiasts. The Staveley lines outlasted the Holwell ones that Stanton had taken over, but in the end they too went over to lorry haulage, adding to the complexities of history, as the following pages tell.

WALTHAM QUARRIES
Owners: Waltham Iron Ore Co

Ironstone is stated to have been discovered at Waltham-on-the-Wolds by William Firth, a colliery owner of Leeds, in the early 1860s[1] but, as with the similar discovery by A.E. Knipe, nothing came of it immediately because of the lack of transport facilities, and the place next appears in the records in May 1881, when Staveley were pushing ahead with their Eastwell properties; it was reported to the board that James Oakes & Co Ltd. had 'taken stone' (presumably samples) from the adjoining property and were willing for Staveley to join them in the venture, a course to which the landowner, the Duke of Rutland, had no objection. Negotiations proceeded on these lines, with George Bond acting for Oakes and Mr Pochin for Staveley, and a lease for about 785 acres in the parishes of Waltham and Eaton was acquired for 49 years from 25th December 1881, with a royalty of 8d per ton. In expectation of considerable traffic, the Great Northern Railway constructed a branch line to Waltham from Scalford Junction on the Joint Great Northern-London & North Western Melton Mowbray-Nottingham line, and even opened a passenger station at the terminus, though the latter was sited primarily with the freight traffic in mind; and the passenger station never had a regular service. The ironstone company's contribution consisted of a narrow gauge tramway running roughly south-east from a tipping stage alongside a siding in the station yard, embanked at the railway end but in a cutting twelve feet deep in the neighbourhood of the quarries east of the Waltham-Lings Hill road[2], which was tunnelled under.

Production commenced in 1882, according to MS, but had ceased by April 1885 because of the poor quality of the ore[3]. As a result, the Duke of Rutland agreed to modification of the lease, with the surrender of the 538 acres 3 roods in Waltham parish and the addition of 825 acres 14 roods in the parish of Branston, and the royalty to be 7½d; these changes to apply from 29th September 1885. Documentary information on the tramway is lacking but the probabilities are that it was similar in essentials to the one to which the company transferred its activities in 1885, and which was to become so well-known to enthusiasts in later years; indeed, the whole outfit was probably taken up and relaid at the new site, and the end-on tipping dock at Waltham is consistent with this theory. Haulage on the tramway was presumably by horses for most of the time. The dates of construction of the first locomotives used at the Eaton site are not known with certainty, but were probably in the period 1884-86, in which case one could have been originally intended for the Waltham site; it is just possible that one did in fact work here but we have no confirmation of this. We can however take it that the tramway was of metre gauge.

The embankment remains, and the site of the tipping dock (high up, as at the Eaton site) but the cutting and quarry have been filled in and the fields levelled; from the latter the upper part of the arch of the bridge beneath the road can be seen and the parapets – known locally as 'the brick walls' – reveal the site of the bridge to passers-by.

An area close to the LNER line was worked for surface limestone by the Barnstone Cement Co Ltd from 1931 to 1941. The main attraction here for locomotive enthusiasts was that the wagons at the sidings were marshalled by a petrol locomotive (MR 2033 of 1920) that had formerly been Lancashire & Yorkshire Railway departmental engine No.3; she finished up at Synthite Ltd, Mold.

Footnotes

1. D.L. Franks, 'The Great Northern and London & North Western Railway Joint Railway.' 1974.
2. A.J. Jukes-Brown: 'Geology of the South-West part of Lincolnshire, with parts of Leicestershire and Nottinghamshire.' Geological Survey Memoirs, 1885, p.49.
3. ibid, p.47.

Grid References

799267	Tipping dock
803262	Bridge under main road

Waltham Quarries (Waltham Iron Ore Co). The 'brick walls' on the Melton Mowbray-Grantham road; the parapet of the former bridge that enabled the Waltham Iron Ore Co to reach ground on the east side of the road. The stone was poor however, and production ceased by 1885, and work was transferred to the Eaton area. 5th April 1953. Eric Tonks

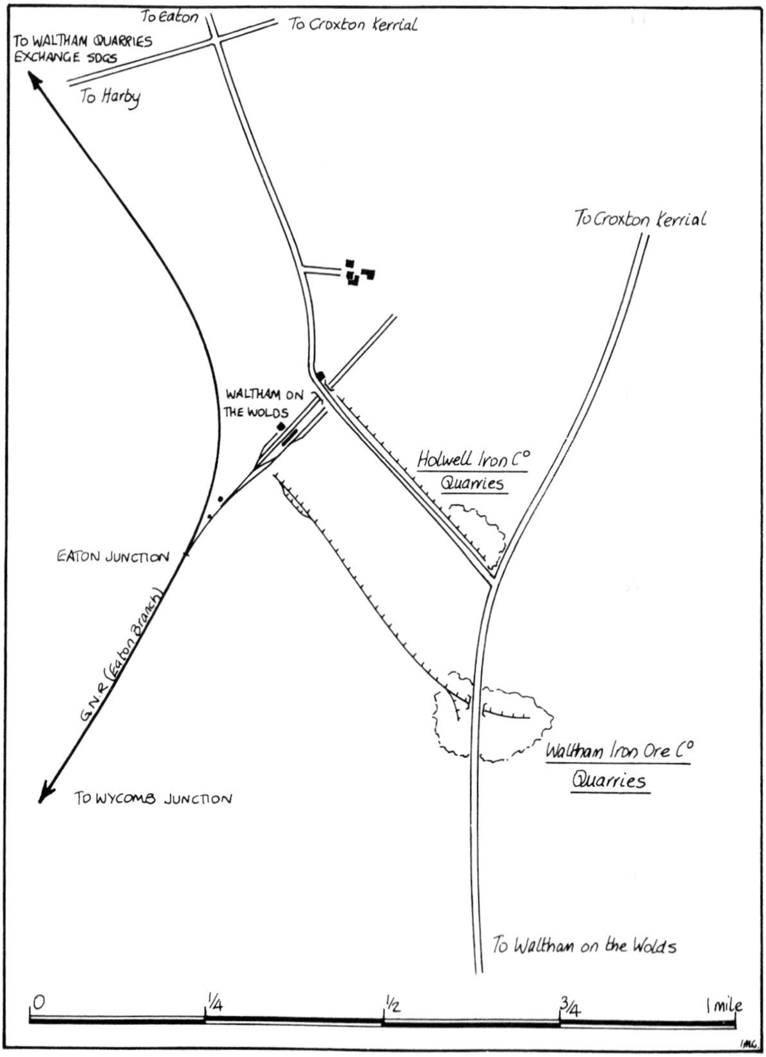
To Eaton
To Croxton Kerrial
TO WALTHAM QUARRIES
EXCHANGE SDGS
To Harby
To Croxton Kerrial
WALTHAM ON
THE WOLDS
Holwell Iron C°
Quarries
EATON JUNCTION
G.N.R (Eaton Branch)
Waltham Iron Ore C°
Quarries
TO WYCOMB JUNCTION
To Waltham on the Wolds
0
1/4
1/2
3/4
1 mile
IMG.

WALTHAM QUARRIES
Owners: Holwell Iron Co Ltd

The Holwell Iron Co obtained from the Duke of Rutland a lease, to work ironstone at Waltham-on-the-Wolds, dated 14th August 1882 – the same year as the Waltham Iron Ore Company's lease, and the quarries were similarly short-lived. Hewlett quotes 1883 as the year when operations commenced, and Jukes-Brown[1] gives the quarries as closed by April 1885. MS, on the other hand, quotes production in 1885-86 only. It is possible to suggest reasons for these discrepancies, but wiser simply to accept the essential that the quarries were technically unsuccessful.

The Holwell Company's quarries lay on the opposite side of the road to the Waltham Company's workings, and seem to have been on an even smaller scale. The tramway is shown on the OS surveyed in 1883 and shows a simple line running end-on to a tipping stage at Waltham-on-the-Wolds station; the wagons therefore would be end-tippers. There are two short references in geological works; A.J. Jukes-Brown[2] refers to the 'examination of the Holwell Iron Company's tramway bearing south-east from the railway bridge,' while a later reference[3] states that 'the cutting is filled in but appears to have run along the south-west side of the by-road trending south-east from the railway bridge . . . A small well was sunk at the office of the Holwell Iron Company's works in the railway cutting on the north-east side of the road at Waltham station, five chains from the centre of the railway' (Actually the line ran on the *north-east* side of the road). No other official information has survived. It is however quite likely that on closure the equipment was sent to Eaton quarries, opened up about the time Waltham closed; if so, the tramway would be of 3ft 1in gauge, and horse-worked. Unlike the Waltham Company's pits, the Holwell workings did not extend beyond the main road, and there are no traces of them or of the tramway to be seen today.

Footnotes

1. A.J. Jukes-Brown; Geology of the South-West part of Lincolnshire, with parts of Leicestershire and Nottinghamshire. Geological Survey Memoirs, 1885, p.47.
2. ibid, p.49.
3. G.W. Lamplugh, W. Gibson, C.B. Wedd, R.L. Sherlock, B. Smith; Geology of Melton Mowbray. Geological Survey Memoirs, 1909, pp.57/8.

Grid References

801269	Tipping dock
804266	Terminus by road

WALTHAM QUARRIES

Owners: Waltham Iron Ore Co Ltd: Eastwell & Waltham Ironstone Co Ltd from 1st April 1957.

The quarries associated in the minds of quarrymen and enthusiasts with the name Waltham Iron Ore Co lay in the parishes of Eaton and Branston on ground leased from the Duke of Rutland; the company started at Waltham-on-the-Wolds, as we have seen, and retained their original title when operations were translated to the new site. The title at the heading is therefore justified by usage and also distinguishes the workings from Stanton's Eaton quarries. The Waltham quarry system lay at the end of the Eaton branch and was undoubtedly one of the most interesting and picturesque by reason of the curious assortment of locomotives acquired to work its metre gauge tramway and by its elevated position commanding throughout a fine panorama of the tree-lined escarpment from the Terrace Hills to the precincts of Belvoir Castle.

The company was jointly promoted by Staveley Coal & Iron Co Ltd and James Oakes & Co Ltd., with the former assuming management. The precise date when operations began here is not certain; MS quotes 1882 onwards without a break, and without distinction between the two sites, but the GNR Eaton branch was built in 1884/85 – again we do not know the date any more closely – evidently in the knowledge of the Waltham Iron Ore Company's proposals to work the Terrace Hills area, which must almost certainly have been under way in 1884, i.e. while the *true* Waltham pits were still in production. There is no reason why this should not have been the case; the original lease covered the area in Eaton parish concerned, the revised lease of 29th September 1885 only substituting Branston for Waltham. It rather looks as if the original intention of Staveley and Oakes was to operate the two sites, but because of the poor quality of the Northampton Sand ironstone at Waltham proper, these pits were closed in 1885, the year in which the new ones in the Marlstone were opened. Hewlett quotes 1885; so does the contemporary account in the 'Midland Naturalist'[1], with a reference to Staveley and Oakes's workings at 'Swainsby's Lodge' (actually Swains Lodge, later Terrace Hills Farm) about one mile north of the Holwell company's workings at Eaton.

The Eaton branch passed beneath the Eastwell-Belvoir road to its terminus on the north-west side, and the Waltham company's leases covered a wide area of ground to the north and west between the road and the Marlstone escarpment, and also to the south and east towards Branston. It is surprising that the tramway serving the quarries was of metre gauge instead of the three feet used at the neighbouring and contemporaneous Staveley-managed system at Eastwell; just another example of the independence of the Staveley units, perhaps, that almost certainly originated at the Waltham quarries proper. In other respects – wagons and the first two locomotives – the equipment was very similar to that at Eastwell; there was no cable-worked incline, but a raised tipping dock on the west side of the Eaton branch a couple of hundred yards short of the terminus, and very similar to the Loddington quarry arrangements that it pre-dated. The artificial embankment up to the tipping stage was shrouded in a sombre group of pines and evergreens, doubtless planted as a windshield as at Hanging Houghton, as the Terrace Hills area is rather exposed and bleak in winter. 150 yards short of the stage the tramway divided, the upper tracks leading to the stage, and the lower to the locomotive shed and office; most of the buildings were of green or red corrugated iron, but there was one workshop of black slatted wood that may have been already on the site. The tipping stage was hand-operated, the steel tubs (6ft 2in by 6ft 6in wide by 3ft 2in deep, and holding 35-37cwt of ore) being pushed one at a time into a wooden cradle and overturned to shoot the load in to a rail wagon beneath the timber supports of the tippler. The empties were then collected to form a train for the return trip to the quarries. There was also in later years a bogie coal wagon kept near the loco shed; Loddington had a similar wagon, probably dating from the World War I period. The wagon dimensions quoted apply to those in use in later years; the original ones, like those at Eastwell, were smaller, carrying just over one ton of ore (as described in Charles Markham's diaries, extracted by Ken Plant).

Operations commenced on both sides of the tippler embankment, working towards the escarpment in both cases, i.e. clockwise on the south-west side and anti-clockwise on the north-east. The former set reached as far as the road – at first the Belvoir road, then Green Lane ('Tofts Lane') running from the road to the escarpment, and in later years at least this quarry was called Green Lane pit. The face on the other side of the tippler also reached the Belvoir road except where prevented by farm buildings and thence in an irregular line across the fields at the back of Swain's Lodge; a likely name for this quarry in early days would be Swain's Lodge pit, but latterly it was known as Long Hole. Between the two a narrow wedge of ground towards the escarpment, in line with the

Waltham Quarries. The quarries were at the end of the GNR Eaton branch and shown here is the tipping arrangement where metre gauge wagons emptied their loads into railway wagons. Note the windshield along the staging; further back the embankment was protected by a belt of trees for the same purpose. The branch terminus lies to the right. 9th July 1957.
J.R. Bonser

Waltham Quarries. The wagon tippler with a metre gauge wagon being emptied. A very similar device was installed at Loddington in Northamptonshire. 20th April 1960.
S.A. Leleux

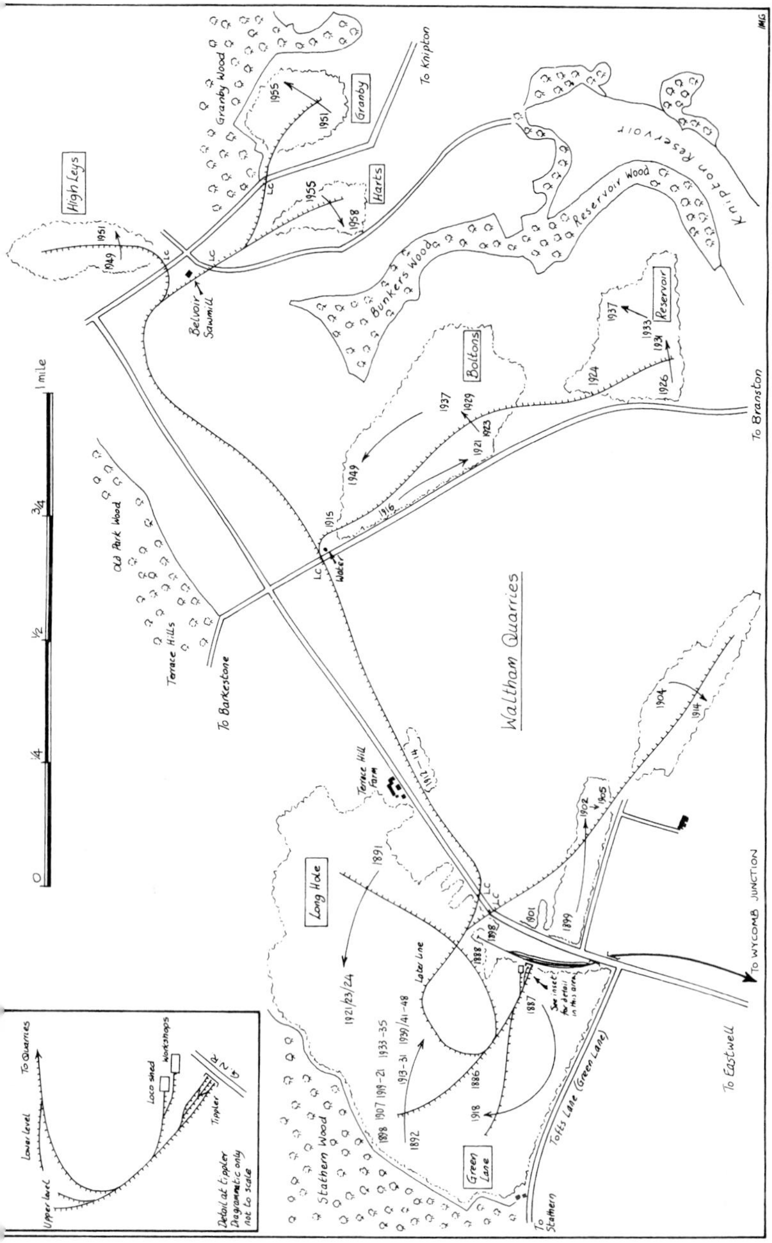
Waltham Quarries
High Leys
Granby
Harts
Boltons
Reservoir
Long Hole
Green Lane
Granby Wood
Reservoir Wood
Knipton Reservoir
Bunkers Wood
Old Park Wood
Terrace Hills
Statherns Wood
Belvoir Sawmill
Terrace Hill Farm
To Knipton
To Branston
To Barkestone
To Eastwell
To Stathern
TO WYCOMB JUNCTION
Tofts Lane (Green Lane)
Later Line
See inset for detail in this area
LC
Water
0
1/4
1/2
3/4
1 mile
Lower level
Upper level
To Quarries
Loco shed
Workshops
Tippler
G.N.R.
Detail at tippler
Diagrammatic only
not to scale

embankment to the tippler, was worked in the 1890s. It might be noted that none of these workings encroached on Stathern Wood on the escarpment slopes, nor did the neighbouring workings of the Holwell Company at Duke's and Hurst's pits; possibly there was a clause in the leases to this effect. Smaller operations east of the Belvoir road commenced in the closing years of the century, and were served by a branch tramway that passed round the end of the Eaton branch, crossed the road on the level and extended along the north-east edge of the spur of high ground, the rest of which was later developed by the Holwell Company as their Beastall's pit. As already referred to under the latter heading, the Waltham Company's workings were relatively shallow and the two narrow pits were worked out by 1914; the more distant of the two was part of Branston Glebe, leased in 1904 for five years, but extended to ten years.

Up to this time, all quarrying activities were within a mile of the tippler, and during World War I production was maintained at Green Lane and Long Hole pits, while a large new area was opened up on the north side of the road from Swain's Lodge to Branston (Branston Lane). Commencing about 1910, a new branch tramway was laid, leaving the Branston Glebe line at a junction west of the Belvoir road, crossing the latter by a separate level crossing and then running parallel with the road most of the way towards Branston Lane, also crossed on the level. Two intermediate crossings with farm tracks were protected by cattle grids. On the north side of this crossing was placed a 'sausage' water tank on concrete piers. A very small amount of ore was obtained en route opposite Terrace Hills Farm, but the main production started beyond Branston Lane at a quarry variously referred to as Bolton's – possibly the occupier of the land – (in GSM) Branston North or Top End (in LI); the latter names arose when the tramway was extended south-east to open up Reservoir Wood quarry, alongside the same road but nearer to Branston. Production at Bolton's and Reservoir Wood quarries commenced about 1915 and 1924 respectively.

The four quarries then in operation sufficed until after World War II, so it is time we had a look at the locomotive stock, which was of extraordinary interest, every machine being of unusual design. First and foremost were the original pair, a photograph of one of which appeared on the office wall at Eastwell, and as our earliest information derives from this photograph, its history is worthy of mention. Maurice Billington obtained a copy from Driver Bird of Coventry Colliery but who had previously been with the Eastwell Iron Ore Company; the original was taken by a Mr C.E. Manchester of Melton Mowbray, and we paid a visit to Cromwell Street, only to learn that Mr Manchester had been killed by a motor-cycle 28 years before. Mrs Manchester, a hale and hearty lady of 82, was sorry she could not help, but some years previously she had destroyed her husband's vast collection of photographs other than those of personal interest; as the collection was almost entirely devoted to local history subjects, there can be little doubt that it contained many others of the quarries in the vicinity – a sad loss indeed.

No-one seemed to know who built the locomotives, but old quarrymen remembered a similar pair of engines at Eastwell, which Staveley stated[1] they had built themselves, JOHN GREEN in 1880 and BELVOIR in 1885; but they had no record of building the Waltham machines. This was the state of our knowledge when IRTM was published, but important discoveries since have enabled us to pursue further enquiries; first, by Roger West, of a photograph of BELVOIR working at Eastwell, and second, by Peter Hawkins, of the personal diaries of Charles (later Sir Charles) Markham, Managing Director of Staveley Coal & Iron Co Ltd. The former settled conclusively that the Eastwell and Waltham locomotives were of the same basic design and suggesting they were by the same builder; in the second source, passed to us by Ken Plant, Charles Markham describes the Eastwell locomotives in considerable mechanical detail but gives no date of construction, nor any mention of the Waltham pair – but he does give the vital information that the boilers were supplied by Clayton & Shuttleworth Ltd, of Lincoln, whose surviving records were at the Museum of English Rural Life at Reading, as we learnt from Jim Hutchinson. Mr D.C. Phillips, the Librarian and Archivist, kindly allowed us to inspect these; meanwhile, Roger West, who had learnt of the existence of a great number of C. & S. mechanical drawings saved by Tom Paisley and stored at the old works of Marshall & Sons Ltd, of Gainsborough, was able, with the help of Ray Hooley, of Lincoln, to examine those relating to the Staveley boilers. Staveley's part in building these locomotives is fully established but – as always – some questions are left unanswered; for a full account of these researches and discussion on the doubtful points, see the article by Eric Tonks and Roger West in 'The Industrial Railway Record' (to be published).

The boilers of the Waltham locomotives were larger than those of the Eastwell pair, and were probably built in 1884 and 1886; very likely it was intended to install one of them at the Waltham-on-the-Wolds quarries

Waltham Quarries. The first two locomotives were of a design unique to these and Eastwell quarries. They had vertical cylinders but carried no makers' plates. Recent research has established that they were built by Staveley in the 1880s. Photographed near the loco shed.
G.F. Manchester

Waltham Quarries. DREADNOUGHT was a standard Manning Wardle 0-4-0ST purchased new in 1910 to operate the new line to Branston. In 1935 the locomotive was fitted with a pair of trailing wheels supplied by Kitsons (who had taken over the MW Goodwill). Photographed on the Branston line just east of the level crossing on 30th June 1952.
K. Cooper/IRS Collection

and the other at the Eaton quarries, and the earlier locomotive could indeed have worked briefly at the former site. The names commemorate George Bond, the Waltham Iron Ore Co Agent (he died in April 1896 and was succeeded by his nephew G.C. Bond); and the landowner, the Duke of Rutland. The close comparison with the names of the Eastwell locomotives will be noted.

The Staveley locomotives, like so many of unorthodox design, were not very successful, it seems; one is believed to have gone shortly after the arrival of DREADNOUGHT, the other probably when THE BARONET came. An inventory of Staveley-owned locomotives dated October 1932 lists only DREADNOUGHT and THE BARONET. One informant stated that one of the Staveley-built engines went on loan to Loddington for a short time in the early 1930s; but at Loddington the staff stated definitely that it was 'DREADNOUGHT, the Manning Wardle' that came from Waltham; and the six-monthly reports of James Fletcher at Loddington quarries suggest that the need for a spare engine was in the late 1920s.

DREADNOUGHT came new from Manning Wardle in 1910 to help with the new extension to Branston, and was the newest locomotive owned by the company; she was a four-coupled saddle tank of typical Manning Wardle appearance, but in 1935 she was provided at the company's shops with a pair of solid-centred trailing wheels supplied in that year by Kitsons, who had acquired the Manning Wardle goodwill. This was to give greater stability. The livery of this engine in 1950 was green with two linings, an outer of black edged with red, and an inner of yellow, while the wheels were green lined red and the coupling rods red; she was probably so turned out by the makers. After overhaul in 1956 the livery was plain green with red rods. The nameplates of brass with red background had block letters after the Hunslet style and not the usual Manning Wardle type with square serifs. The selection of the name is not explained. Mr Coy retained one of the plates after she was cut up.

Three further locomotives were acquired second-hand, the first being a Markham from Loddington (probably in the late 1920s) and originally at Cranford until standard gauge was introduced there; this little engine, neat and sturdy but hardly pretty with its squat riveted tank, stovepipe chimney and lacking any cab, remained virtually unaltered throughout its life and on withdrawal from service in 1949 still carried 'Cranford Ironstone Co' on brass plates on the tank, while the nameplates proper were attached to the bunker; these plates were unusual in lacking a raised surround. The locomotive was in 1949 relegated to a siding a few

Waltham Quarries. Later locomotives were all secondhand, the first being THE BARONET, built by Markham for Cranford quarries in 1888. A ruggedly simple design with minimum protection for the driver. For this reason perhaps she was not popular on the exposed Belvoir plateau, and from 1949 was relegated to the sidings behind the locomotive shed amid discarded wagons. 22nd April 1958. P.D.Rowbotham

hundred yards from the shed together with some discarded wagons. The livery was green with yellow inner and red, edged with black, outer lining.

In September 1944 HOLWELL No. 6 was borrowed from Eaton quarries for a brief period, when presumably the Waltham locos were all out of commission, and necessitating a quick change of gauge from three feet. The next regular acquisition was of a Corpet Louvet six-coupled side tank, generally similar to CAMBRAI at Loddington and painted green, lined black edged with red; it still carried its original number and name plates (with lettering of unusual form) and the makers' plate was one of the few cast when the firm was owned by Veuve ('widow') Corpet and L. Louvet. This engine NANTES was well-liked by the crew, who had mastered the French instructions, and with DREADNOUGHT worked the whole of the traffic from 1949 to 1956. In 1956 DREADNOUGHT required heavy overhaul and CAMBRAI, the only other French steam locomotive on British soil, was brought from Loddington to replace her, being specially repainted green with red nameplates and rods. She had some teething troubles at Waltham and for a time DREADNOUGHT had to carry on. When DREADNOUGHT was repaired, NANTES was withdrawn from service and dumped on a spur off the line to the tippler, leaving DREADNOUGHT and CAMBRAI to deal with the traffic.

Waltham Quarries. NANTES was obtained from France in 1934 and was one of the few locomotives plated 'Veuve Corpet and L. Louvet'. She was well-liked at Waltham and is shown at work with the wagons being loaded by a small Ruston Bucyrus shovel in the Knipton area (probably Granby Wood quarry). 19th March 1954. J.R. Bonser

Waltham Quarries. In 1956 NANTES was joined by CAMBRAI, the other Corpet Louvet in ironstone service, at Loddington. Here she is in the sidings behind the shed in September 1957. M.J. Lee

We have dealt with the locomotives all together for convenience but must now go back to the history of the quarries 'between the wars'. There was the usual drop in requirements from Waltham after World War I and it seems that the entire undertaking was closed down for about a year in the 1921-22 period, but was then resumed at the same three faces – Green Lane, Long Hole, and Bolton's. The first two were working towards each other and operations at Long Hole ceased in 1925; but in the previous year Reservoir Wood quarry was opened up and was worked continuously until exhausted in 1937. Quarrying was taken to the edge of the outcrop where the ground falls away to the valley of the Devon. Operations were then moved back to Bolton's quarry, which had been standing since 1929, and continued to 1949. An interesting note on the surveyor's 'face plan' of Bolton's quarry reads 'Commenced loading with navvy 18/6/1937.'

Waltham Iron Ore Company had very little overburden to contend with and their first machine was obtained in 1934, a 15-ton Ruston shovel; she probably worked in the Reservoir Wood quarry until closure in 1937, and then moved to Bolton's. Details of only two other machines are known, a 21RB shovel and a 24RB shovel, acquired in 1939 and 1940 respectively. The 24RB was converted to a dragline in 1944 and the pattern of working then was for the 24RB to perform the baring and the 21RB the loading. According to Mr Kemp, Area Manager in later years, there may have been a second 24RB, but this has not been identified.

The intensive working of World War II, when all three locomotives – THE BARONET, DREADNOUGHT and NANTES – were in regular use, practically exhausted the quarries then in operation; the last cut of the former Green Lane quarry, referred to in LI as 'Northern Terrace Hills quarry', was made in 1948, and at 'Branston North' (formerly Bolton's) in 1949. The old steam digger was moved to where the line from the tipping dock began its sweeping curve back towards the road; at this point there was a stockpile of ore, probably built up when demand was slack so that output could be maintained when operations were hampered by snow, for example. One line circled round the foot of this ore dump, with the digger at the end, and another line circled in the opposite direction on a shelf, rather like a crab in difficulties. Normal production was maintained from a series of quarries near the Eastwell-Knipton road. The first of these quarries, High Leys, was reached by a tramway extension starting at the level crossing on the Branston lane, then running for most of its way parallel to the road to Knipton. At High Leys itself the road makes a right angle turn from north-east to south-east in a small valley, and the tramway was carried round this bend on an embankment, offering wonderful scenic opportunities to the photographer. The line then crossed the road to the quarry on the east side, which was worked from 1949 to 1951. The two diesel machines from Bolton's quarry worked successively in High Leys, Granby Wood and Harts quarries (see below), it is believed.

Two other quarries were opened up, one on each side of the road to Knipton, almost half way between High Leys and the road junction south-east of Knipton; the road dips steeply to the village and the quarries were on the outcrop, like the old Reservoir Wood quarry. The tramway was extended across the bridleway to Knipton Reservoir en route, with a branch across the road to Granby Wood quarry – again via a level crossing on this not very busy road. Granby Wood quarry was worked 1951-55 while Hart's quarry on the south-west side of the road was worked 1955-58. The total tramway distance to the tipping dock was just over three miles, and it was possibly the combination of long haulage with relatively small output that caused the closure of Hart's quarry in February 1958, a time of depression in the iron ore industry. The closure

Waltham Quarries. The mainly shallow overburden of the Belvoir area did not require much in the way of quarry machinery. The No. 15 steam navvy was obtained in 1934 and worked in the Branston area quarries, finishing up at the ore stockpile behind the locomotive shed, where she was photographed on 28th March 1956. J.R. Bonser

Waltham Quarries. The Marlstone ironstone appeared as outcrop on the top of the Belvoir escarpment, exposed to the winds on all sides, and it could be a bleak place for working, notwithstanding the trees along the edge. The atmosphere is caught well in this photograph of DREADNOUGHT coming across the embankment from High Leys towards the Branston road level crossing on 29th March 1955. J.R. Bonser

Waltham Quarries. A cuckoo in the nest! Standard gauge P 1952 stands on the Waltham dock after a repaint, before taking up its duties at Mill Hill quarries. 1957. H. Gray

was described in the press as 'temporary' and there was some talk of reopening with lorry haulage, but nothing came of this and the men were found work in other nearby quarries.

The working locomotives CAMBRAI and DREADNOUGHT were greased up and locked in the shed. NANTES, already withdrawn, was left outside on the bank to the tipplers. Silhouetted amongst the trees, her typical French outline presented a most unusual spectacle to the casual passer-by – but she was familiar enough to the enthusiasts who flocked to 'Waltham.' In May 1958 the burners arrived, but they did nothing beyond cutting up a few of the 'trams' that had been keeping THE BARONET company down the line, and then decamped. Road trimmers severed the rail at the level crossing in the same month, but for the next 12 months nothing was touched; a little sugar beet traffic used the tipping dock, which was otherwise deserted. A fence was placed across the track between NANTES and THE BARONET; a bush sprouted between the latter's frames and weeds grew over her. In August 1959 track lifting by road vehicles commenced, and by December all track had been lifted from Knipton right back to the level crossing near the shed. Some rail was sold to the Hoveringham Gravel Co Ltd. and to Richard Thomas & Baldwin's

Irthingborough mines, and this was sent away in lorries of the Syston Haulage Co. After further lifting of the track to the fence below NANTES, a halt was made to restore the ground to its original contours where the tramway crossed arable land. One tippler was cut up by July and wagons were being scrapped rapidly, but 61 remained when the Birmingham Locomotive Club paid final homage on 28th August 1960. A large party assembled and enough eager hands were available to push DREADNOUGHT and CAMBRAI out of the shed. The sun came out and shone through the trees and drifting gossamer clouds of willow herb seeds; then back went the engines.

Come October all track had gone save a length outside the locomotive shed where the three engines lay huddled, DREADNOUGHT between the two Frenchmen, and a short length on the top of the dock used for storing wagons before they were scrapped. An attempt was made to bring THE BARONET to join the others, but she was too rusted to move and finished ignominiously on her nose about a hundred yards away. By Armistice Day 'Eric the Burner' Burroughs of Ketton had his acetylene equipment on the spot and soon despatched THE BARONET, followed by NANTES. The latter had been donated to the Talyllyn Railway Preservation Society for their narrow gauge museum at Towyn, and one

Waltham Quarries. After closure in 1958 DREADNOUGHT and CAMBRAI were left in the loco.shed (left) but NANTES was put on the embankment (right) for collection by the Tal-y-Llyn RPS. But there were delays in arranging transport and NANTES suffered from exposure, as a result of which it was CAMBRAI that was saved, and NANTES was cut up.

G.P. Roberts

works plate had already been sent there, but the Society was unable to find the costs of transport and the engine was now beyond economic repair. Accordingly the company generously offered instead CAMBRAI, which had enjoyed better protection, and she was despatched to Towyn the first week in December, after being hauled over the field and across BR metals by a lorry from Eastwell – a strange sight indeed! The chimney off NANTES accompanied her to Towyn. DREADNOUGHT was the last to be scrapped, in December, and by Christmas every scrap of track had been lifted, even in the shed. Down the course of the line a bare patch showed where THE BARONET had lain for a decade and, beyond the curve, the derelict steam digger ready to take another bite at the bank of ore remaining. The course of the line could then be followed across the road, then a few hundred yards over rough fields until ploughed land was reached.

Waltham Quarries. The corner at High Leys; the road in the foreground turns through a right angle to run in front of the trees, with the tramway on the embankment. The tramway is in course of removal on 27th April 1960, using the 24RB dragline. We have walked this road a score of times, toiling up the long winding hill from Knipton. D.H. Newman

The digger was not cut up for some time; she was sold to Eric Burroughs in 1961 and scrapped by him some while afterwards. The wagons, of which there had been about two hundred at one time, were cut up in 1960, except for one that was left on the trackbed by the crossing of the bridleway to Knipton Reservoir. This wagon had been used at the loco shed as a container for ashes and in 1963 was taken into the adjacent timber yard, and shavings burnt in it from time to time. There was a scheme in 1966 to preserve this wagon at Lincoln Technical College at the suggestion of Mr Nevill Birch, but in view of the existence of the similar Eastwell specimen, we recommended that one of the Greetwell wagons be saved instead. The Waltham wagon was by then in very poor condition, with earth and weeds growing in the body, but it was not cut up until about 1973.

While the trackbed was cleared very quickly, there seemed to be no hurry to deal with the remains at headquarters; at the end of 1960 Mr Poyser, the quarry manager, stated that all the buildings were to go 'except the black shed', but it was another seven years before this came about. The tippler gantry was taken down at the same time but the embankment was left and – as promised –'the black shed'. The BR track was lifted in the middle 1960s, and about 1970 the awkward road bridge, was removed, to the benefit of motorists. Early in 1980 the embankment of the BR branch terminus was cleared of trees that had grown up, and was used for stacking hay bales etc. The embankment of the Waltham tramway was still extant, however, trees included, and with a few sleepers as well as sleeper marks. Beyond this point nothing can be seen of the wide tramway loop towards the road, but there are traces on the east side; faint in the case of the early line towards Sherricliffe Farm, but unmistakable for the later one towards Branston Lane, with a clearly defined course over the hummocky ground, ablaze with nodding thistles and ragwort in summer. Beyond this rough patch the ploughed fields show no sign, and the fields west of the road near Terrace Hills Farm show only shallow depressions where the ore was removed. The Branston Lane level crossing is marked by the concrete base of the water tank, but there are no traces of the quarrying areas of Bolton's and Reservoir Wood quarries. Part of the trackbed to Reservoir Wood quarry can be seen as an overgrown ledge east of the lane.

Traces of the tramway can be picked up again in the vicinity of High Leys. The fine embankment round the inner side of the sharp bend in the road has been smoothed over into the grass fields, but the ledge on the

Waltham Quarries. The tree-clad embankment leading to the tippler site, with the one remaining wooden shed (right) and the BR trackbed in the centre of the picture. 18th July 1985.
Eric Tonks

Waltham Quarries. The supports of the water tank by the Branston lane level crossing, looking towards High Leys. 18th July 1985.
Eric Tonks

hillside towards the sawmill is clear, and the lineside hedge at the latter still stands. Of the level crossing where the branch to High Leys quarry crossed the road there is not a trace, and the quarry itself has been smoothed over. There are however some remains of the last two quarries. At Hart's the terminal gullet has been left, and the extent of quarrying can be judged by the sunken ground, including a portion of replacement hedge. Across the road, Granby Wood quarry has been filled in and is now a plantation, but running up to the field gate entrance is a causeway of stone that once carried the tramway; the causeway is overgrown and at one point has been breached, so that one can see the constructional rubble. Opposite the field gate at the corner of Granby Wood are two posts in the hedge, marking the point where the tramway crossed the road to join up with the line from Hart's quarry. A barn by the roadside is a convenient marker from which to investigate. It was said that Granby Wood pit was filled with the spoil from Hart's, leaving the latter in its unfilled condition.

In essence, then, there are visible remains of the Waltham system at the two extremities, and very little in between – not surprising, as the stone was mostly outcrop or under shallow cover; but the countryside of Belvoir is so attractive as to make the effort of seeing these evocative remains rewarding.

Footnotes

1. E. Wilson, 'The Marlstone of Leicestershire as a source of iron'. The Midland Naturalist, 1885.
2. Letter 7th December 1951 from the Mines Office of Staveley Coal & Iron Co Ltd., West Bridgford, Nottingham.

Grid References

790308	Tipping dock
791309	Level crossing with Eastwell-Belvoir road (old)
792310	Level crossing with Eastwell-Belvoir road (new)
797313	Swains Lodge (Terrace Hills farm)
801302	Terminus of working towards Eaton
803316	Level crossing, Branston Lane
810303	Reservoir Wood Pit terminus
811323	High Leys embankment
815314	Hart's pit terminus
813321	Level crossing to High Leys
815318	Level crossing to Granby Wood
823320	Sawmill

Locomotives

Gauge: 1 metre

GEORGE BOND*	0-4-0STG	VC	Staveley		1884			New 1884	Scr
RUTLAND*	0-4-0STG	VC	Staveley		1886			New 1886	Scr
DREADNOUGHT	0-4-2ST (0-4-0ST to 1935)	OC	MW	1757	1910	11 x 17ins	2ft 9ins	New 2/1910	(1)
THE BARONET	0-4-0ST	OC	Mkm	102	1889	8 x 10ins	2ft 0ins	(a)	(2)
54 NANTES	0-6-0T	0C	Veuve Corpet & L Louvet	936	1903	280 x 380mm	950mm	(b)	(3)
CAMBRAI	0-6-OT	OC	L Corpet	493	1888	300 x 450mm	900mm	(c)	(4)
HOLWELL No. 6	0-4-0ST	OC	HC	375	1890	10 x 16ins	2ft 9ins	(d)	(5)

(a) ex Loddington Quarries after 1923
(b) ex Thos W. Ward Ltd, 1934; prev Chemin de Fer de la Loire Inferieure, latterly Societe Sedim
(c) ex Loddington Quarries 3/1956
(d) ex Stanton Ironworks Co Ltd, Holwell Works, 10/1944

(1) to Loddington Quarries c 1910; ex Loddington. Scr on site by Eric Burroughs 12/1960
(2) Scr on site by Eric Burroughs 11/1960
(3) Scr on site by Eric Burroughs 12/1960
(4) to Narrow Gauge Museum, Towyn, 12/1960
(5) to Stanton Ironworks Co Ltd, Eaton Quarries, c 10/1944

* Names may be transposed,

Quarry Machines

No. 15	S. Navvy. Crane. Caterpillar	RH 809	1923	2¼ Cu. Yds.	28ft.		(a)	(1)
21RB	D. Shovel	RB 2999	1936	¾ Cu. Yd.	18ft 6ins		(b)	(2)
24RB	D. Shovel	RB 4951	1940	⅞ Cu. Yd.	18ft 6ins	New 5/1940	(c)	(3)

(a) ex Logan & Hemingway, contractors, Westbury, Wiltshire, 6/1934
(b) ex Chas Jones, dealer, Colwyn Bay, 1939
(c) Converted to dragline 1944, with ½ Cu. Yd, 60ft.

(1) At Reservoir Wood quarry (?); to Bolton's quarry, 6/1937. to Park Gate Iron & Steel Co Ltd, Sproxton Quarries, 1937; ex Sproxton c 1938. At ore dump behind tipping stage. Scr. on site by Eric Burroughs c 1/1962
(2) In Branston quarries; High Leys quarry, 1949-51; Granby Wood quarry 1951-55; Hart's quarry 1955-58. To Eastwell Quarries c 1958
(3) New to Bolton's quarry; High Leys quarry 1949-51; Granby Wood quarry 1951-3. To Sproxton Quarries 4/1953; ex Sproxton 5/1953. Granby Wood quarry 1953-55, Hart's quarry 1955-58. To Sproxton Quarries 7/1958.

EASTWELL QUARRIES

Owners: Eastwell Iron Ore Co; Eastwell Iron Ore Co Ltd; Eastwell & Waltham Ironstone Co Ltd from 1st April 1957: Eastwell & Loddington Ironstone Co Ltd from 1st October 1959; Staveley Minerals Ltd from 7th March 1961.

The Eastwell quarries were opened up after those at Holwell but before the Eaton and Waltham group that followed the building of the Great Northern Railway mineral branches. The Staveley company had been trying to obtain Marlstone ore from this area from soon after its discovery; attempts to obtain a lease of the Holwell area from Howard Allport were thwarted by the formation of the Holwell Iron Co to work these quarries, so Staveley then turned to the nearest accessible area of ironstone. At this time (1879) the only local railway, other than the Midland Railway Nottingham-Peterborough line, was the Great Northern-London & North Western Joint line from Melton Mowbray to Bottesford Junction in the Vale of Belvoir, on the south-east side of which the Marlstone Cliff here forms an imposing escarpment some 250 feet high; on the edge lay an outcrop of ironstone with very extensive reserves to the south. The Staveley Coal & Iron Co Ltd joined forces with the Bestwood Coal & Iron Co Ltd. in opening negotiations in May 1879 with the principal landowner, the Duke of Rutland, but through the same Howard Allport, who appears to have been appointed by the Duke to look after his interests in this field. Following a meeting at Belvoir at the beginning of September 1879 and successful outcome of sample trials[1], the joint companies obtained a lease of 828 acres in the parishes of Eastwell and Goadby Marwood for a period of 52 years from 25th March 1889; the lease carried a break clause (i.e. the lease could be terminated after any seven years subject to one year's notice) and a royalty of 7 1/2d per ton of ironstone was chargeable.

To operate the quarries, the separate Eastwell Iron Ore Company was formed with a committee of management of four (two from each owning company). We have already referred to Staveley's policy of placing their ironstone quarries in the ownership of separate companies, and as Eastwell was the first, it may be useful to explain the position in more detail. Most of the 'Staveley' quarries were in fact jointly owned by combinations of Staveley Coal & Iron Co Ltd with other ironmasters, with Staveley exercising management. The proprietors provided capital and plant to start the quarry companies, which were controlled by an agent who agreed to supply ore at a specified price – initially 1d a ton above the 'getting price'. It follows that the different quarries enjoyed a certain autonomy, preserving their individuality and responsibility for their own affairs to a considerable degree; they did most of their own repairs to machinery and locomotives, for example. (A prime example of this is the repair of the standard gauge Peckett for Mill Hill quarry at the Waltham premises, even though they had no standard gauge track – both quarries being under common ownership). Stanton Ironworks Co Ltd, a company of comparable size and standing, adopted a policy of central control, with all the quarries owned directly by the company, and repairs mostly carried out at central workshops. To the outside enthusiast these different policies revealed themselves in two principal ways. The Staveley quarries tended to exhibit individual characteristics at the start and to retain them largely intact. Stanton, on the other hand, were more uniform in general equipment, but the practice of sending machinery to Stanton or Holwell Works for overhaul meant an ever-changing pattern of these items at the quarries. Locomotives, for example, moved from quarry to shops and on to another quarry, in much the same way as Great Western Railway locomotives were allocated to a different shed after overhaul at Swindon Works. The same applied to quarry machines. In a few words, Staveley quarries were different in equipment, simple in locomotive history; Stanton quarries had more uniform equipment but a more involved locomotive history – for every three transfers of Staveley locomotives, Stanton moved eight. In the post-World War II years, when Stanton management, under the style of Stewarts & Lloyds Minerals Ltd, exerted an increasing control of Staveley affairs, their policy became dominant.

To return to the subject in hand; Eastwell Iron Ore Co was formed in September 1880 but already preparations were under way on the transport side. To convey the stone from the quarries to the main line railway a cable-operated double incline was constructed from a tipping stage alongside 'Stathern Ironstone Siding' (known as 'Eastwell Sidings' until 1887) to a point at the summit about two thirds of a mile west of Eastwell village, from which the tracks were than taken to the working faces. The tramway was of 3-foot gauge and the slope of the incline one in four at the steepest point. Second-hand rails and sleepers for the incline were obtained in August 1880 and construction was pushed forward, loading of ironstone commencing in May 1881 with the completion of the railway sidings the previous month. Outcrop stone close to the top of the incline was worked first, and close by were situated the office, locomotive

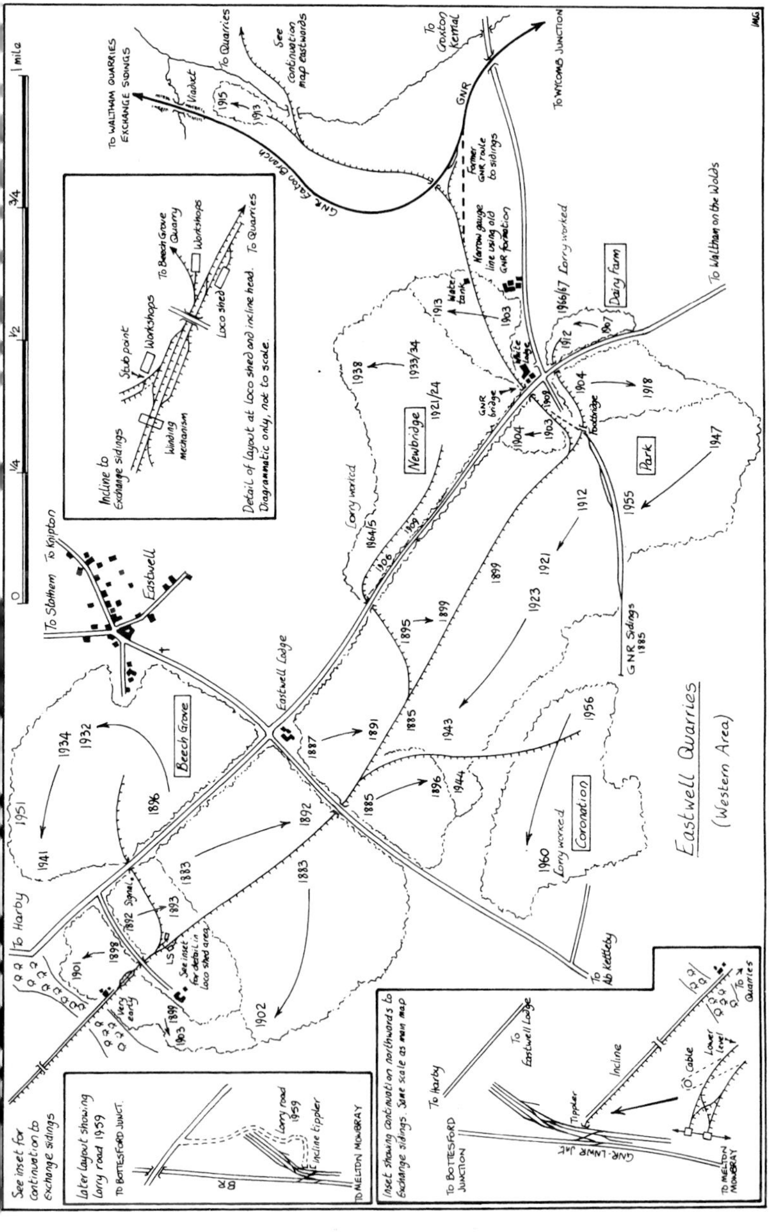
Eastwell Quarries
(Western Area)
0
1/4
1/2
3/4
1 mile
TO WALTHAM QUARRIES EXCHANGE SIDINGS
Viaduct
To Quarries
See continuation map eastwards
To Croxton Kerrial
TO WYCOMB JUNCTION
GNR
GNR Eaton Branch
Former GNR route to sidings
Narrow gauge line using old GNR formation
Water tank
Lorry worked
Dairy Farm
To Waltham on the Wolds
White Lodge
GNR bridge
Footbridge
Newbridge
Park
GNR Sidings 1885
Coronation
Beech Grove
Eastwell Lodge
Eastwell
To Knipton
To Stathern
To Harby
To Ab Kettleby
Signal
LS
See inset for detail in Loco shed area
Very early
Incline to Exchange sidings
Stub point
Workshops
Winding mechanism
To Beech Grove Quarry
Loco shed
To Quarries
Detail of Layout at Loco shed and incline head. Diagrammatic only, not to scale.
See inset for continuation to exchange sidings
Later layout showing lorry road 1959
TO BOTTESFORD JUNCT.
Lorry road 1959
Incline tippler
BR
TO MELTON MOWBRAY
Inset showing continuation northwards to Exchange sidings. Same scale as main map
To Harby
To Eastwell Lodge
Incline
Tippler
Cable
Lower level
To Quarries
TO BOTTESFORD JUNCTION
GNR-LNWR Jnt
TO MELTON MOWBRAY
1883
1885
1887
1891
1892
1893
1895
1896
1898
1899
1901
1902
1903
1904
1906
1907
1908
1909
1912
1913
1915
1918
1921
1921/24
1923
1932
1933/34
1934
1938
1941
1943
1944
1947
1951
1955
1956
1960
1964/5
1966/67
IMG

Eastwell Quarries. Looking down the incline, showing full wagons at left and empties at right. 8th March 1953. C.P. Knight

Eastwell Quarries. View from below the trees lining the escarpment, showing the method of attachment of the wagons to the cable. Note the overbridge further down the slope. 21st April 1960. S.A. Leleux

Eastwell Quarries. The unloading station at the tipping dock to the BR line, 26th March 1960. The wheel for the cable will be noted, and empty wagons standing at left. G.D. King

Eastwell Quarries. The winding house at the head of the incline, 28th August 1960. G.H. Starmer

shed and repair shops. Full wagons were marshalled in sidings in readiness for descending the incline; they were attached singly to the overhead cable by a length of chain, one end of which was attached to the wagon coupling and the other wrapped several times round the cable, while the wagon was held in position by a long horizontal wooden bar pressing against the wagon frame. The wagons were sometimes referred to in early days as 'corves.'

At the foot of the incline each wagon was released from the cable and run into one of two tipplers, emptied and returned to the cable for hauling up by the descending wagons. Movements of the cable were controlled from a wooden structure straddling the lines at the summit, by a brakesman in communication by telephone with the unloading stage; this instrument, one of the first of its kind in commercial use, crude technically but in use for 50 years, was kept for the interest of visitors long after it was superseded by a modern instrument. At the foot of the incline the cable was carried round an idler wheel mounted in a carriage fastened to a tensioning weight. The tipping device was an iron cradle into which the tubs were run one at a time, rotated by means of a braking wheel to empty their contents into a railway wagon below, the tub then being pushed on to another siding for re-attachment to the cable. Wagon handling was all manual, the tracks at the tippler and at the incline head being designed to utilise gravity as far as possible. Railway wagons were released from a stock siding by gravity and, when full, run into another siding for collection. The ironstone tubs were of steel with flared sides and with a large central wooden buffer at each end, and carried one ton of ore. The incline was crossed by two accommodation bridges, one a short way below the belt of trees at the summit and another near the foot; the second one was removed some years later. There was a runaway siding a few yards from the summit.

In 1882 there were complaints of inferior ore; and while this seems to have been only a transitory complaint, it did encourage Staveley in their negotiations for a lease at Waltham along with James Oakes & Co Ltd; the latter company also joined the Staveley/Bestwood partnership in the Eastwell Iron Ore Co on a third-each basis. When the Great Northern laid their Eaton branch, an offshoot was made from a junction about 230 yards north of the bridge over Green Lane (Lings Hill to White Lodge) to serve the Eastwell workings at a tipping dock 1¼ miles south-east of the office. The Eastwell branch was reported in the 'Midland Naturalist' of 1885 as 'nearly complete'; this outlet obviated the labour of cable working but it was never brought into use, possibly because of the inconvenience of unloading at a point remote from the office, or because of a higher freight charge from the new tipping point. The output all went to the owning companies, but Eastwell had power to sell ore to others if they wished. From 25th March 1886 a reduction in royalty to 6d was granted, whether in respect of greater tonnages or because of further murmurings about quality, is unknown; the 7 ½d rate was later restored. In 1894 calcining was considered but not put in to effect.

Day-to-day working altered little, in 1950 being not much different from 1890; the principal source of change was the opening of new quarries and the closure of old ones, with alterations in the tramway to suit, and additions to the locomotive stock when required. Up to 1900 the general trend of quarrying was south-eastwards on both sides of the main tramway, as far as the Eastwell-Waltham road; also, in 1894/5 a branch line was laid from the office area to a quarry on the north-east side of this road. This quarry was not worked so intensively as the others and possibly was kept as reserve for such times as long-distance working was impracticable, as in hard winters. As Beech Grove Quarry, this was operated as late as the 1950s, but the names of quarries before 1900 do not seem to have been recorded.

A small addition to the Duke of Rutland lease is recorded for 1897, but on 25th May 1903 two leases, from the Duke of Rutland and the Marquis of Granby were submitted to the Staveley board for signature; these were for a total of 450 acres in the neighbourhood of White Lodge, Goadby Marwood, on both sides of the Eastwell-Waltham road, and were developed immediately. The course of the GNR Eastwell branch, probably already taken up, provided easy access to the White Lodge area itself, and the ironstone tramway was taken under the GNR bridge to open up quarries on both sides of the tramway. This was in 1903, but in 1906 a shorter access to the main tramway was put in at the north-west end of the northern quarry by a new bridge under the road; this quarry was then referred to as Newbridge Quarry (sometimes rendered as New Bridge, but usually as one word). A small area was opened in 1907 south of the green lane by White Lodge, and was called Dairy Farm quarry, while south-west of the Waltham road was Park quarry. None of these pits were worked continually; Park from 1904 to 1918, then 1944 to 1955; Newbridge up to 1938, then a brief revival in 1964/65; Dairy Farm only worked up to 1912, then in 1966/67 – the last Eastwell quarry to be operated.

When the ironstone tramway was extended along the former GN

Eastwell Quarries. When the GNR built the Eaton branch, a sub-branch was put in to serve the Eastwell quarries; but it was never used as such and the track was subsequently taken up. The bridge however was left and provided easy access for the iron ore company when they wished to extend operations to the Branston area. July 1957. J.R. Bonser

Eastwell Quarries. Though the 'Eastwell Branch' was lifted, a siding was provided by the GNR at the former junction, and the iron ore company laid a siding to this that lasted up to BR days, and occasional use was made of it to bring in or take out items for which the incline was unsuitable. This view was taken on 7th July 1957. Note THE SCOT lying abandoned in the yard, and the crane. J.R. Bonser

trackbed, it was taken as far as the Eaton branch, where an exchange siding was put in with the latter; no ore was transferred here but miscellaneous goods and machinery from the GNR were dealt with. The OS apparently did not note the change of gauge and the 1931 6ins map was captained 'LNER Eastwell Branch'. This error was then further confounded in LI, which gives the Eastwell tramway as of standard gauge because of this 'connection'. How easy it is for simple errors to multiply – but we all make them!

This extension of the narrow gauge tramway gave the Eastwell company access to all the ironstone in the immediate vicinity of Eastwell; between Eastwell and Eaton there is an area of boulder clay filling an ancient valley, and to reach fresh reserves of ironstone it was necessary to lay a lengthy extension – almost doubling the length of the tramway, in fact. On 24th May 1910 Charles Markham informed the Staveley board that negotiations with the Duke of Rutland to acquire the ironstone at Branston had been going on for some time; and there seemed to be some urgency in the matter as, should they not take up the lease, Stanton were anxious to have it. In all, leases for a total of 860 acres were obtained – 700 on the Duke's land at Branston, 105 on Branston Glebe and 55 on Eaton Glebe. The Rutland lease was dated September 1911 and was for 40 years with a royalty on ironstone of 7½d per ton and 3d for limestone; the other leases were signed the same day, 29th August 1911, and the terms were probably similar. Staveley, Bestwood and Oakes each took a third share. There were an estimated four million tons of ore available and it was hoped initially to take 1,000 tons per week – 700 to Staveley and 300 to Oakes – from this area, in effect doubling Eastwell's output.

Before this could be done however it was necessary to lay the tramway extension and attend to other related matters. The tramway extension was not a simple matter of extending the rails over level ground, as it had been up to then; the line had to pass beneath the GNR Eaton branch and then over the valley of the river Devon – crossing the latter by a viaduct – and beneath the Eaton-Waltham road. All this called for considerable movement of earth in cutting and filling, and a temporary two-foot gauge tramway was provided, consisting of light portable track, steel side-tipping wagons, and a small German locomotive, the last from a sewage works contract. This outfit later became a standard piece of Staveley equipment, moved from quarry to quarry as the need arose, and with the well-known PIXIE as locomotive. Not all of it left Eastwell for Pilton (the next known on the list for engineering work) however; eight 'Jubilee' tip wagons and two 'Decauville' wagons were hired to Sproxton in the 1925-28 period, while some wagons and track were left behind and were still under the bridge in Branston village as late as 1976, long after all of Eastwell's three-foot track and wagons had gone.

The equipment for operating the incline was also improved; Markham & Co Ltd supplied housing for the machinery in October 1911 and a 'wheel frame with pulley' in June 1912. At the foot of the incline a second tippler gantry was installed so that there was a pair of cradles over each of the two sidings. When the negotiations for the new leases were in the final stage, the company asked the GNR to improve the facilities at 'the sidings at Eastwell'; from the specific reference to the GNR only, it is just possible that the original intention was to use the exchange sidings at the Eaton branch, but in fact the Stathern sidings were used, comprising extra sidings for empty and full wagons, and the GNR-LNWR Officers' Joint Committee reported that the new layout was brought into use on 25th October 1912 [2]. On 29th October the Staveley company likewise reported that the Branston extension was 'almost complete'. New wagons of larger size were ordered and became standard from then on, gradually replacing the older type; dimensions were 5ft 7ins by 6ft 6ins by 3ft 0ins deep, and containing 30-35cwt. of ore, and the new tippler was built to suit them. The last small wagons were in use in 1940. Two more locomotives were obtained, including the first six-wheeler for the longer haul to Branston. At this point therefore it is useful to look at the locomotive stock.

The first locomotives were built by Staveley, two of the very few locomotives designed specifically for ironstone work; they were basically similar to the two at Waltham quarries, the essential features of which were known from a photograph that hung on the office wall at Eastwell. Since then, a photograph of one of the Eastwell machines has come to light, confirming the general similarity in build and revealing a few differences; while very full dimensions have turned up in the diaries of Charles Markham, managing director of the Staveley company. The cylinders are vertical, and the drive geared in the ratio 13 to 32; the boilers were supplied by Clayton & Shuttleworth of Lincoln, from whole files further information was obtained, as described under the Waltham section. The names of these locomotives were of local significance, JOHN GREEN being the Duke of Rutland's agent when Eastwell started operations, and the other being named BELVOIR. The next two locomotives were conventional Hudswell Clarke 0-4-0STs; the name LORD GRANBY (the title of the heir to the Duke) referred to the

Eastwell Quarries. Newbridge quarry, about 1931, with typical plank and barrow operation. The wagons are of the smaller and earlier type. Note 'step-faulting' of the rock. BGS

Eastwell Quarries. The early locomotives were all four-wheelers, including two Hudswell Clarkes. THE SCOT (origin of name not known) was photographed 3rd September 1947. Sister loco LORD GRANBY is in Leeds Industrial Museum. G. Alliez/Courtesy B.D. Stoyel

Eastwell Quarries. The discovery of this photograph by Roger West proved a decisive factor in establishing the origin of these strange locomotives at Eastwell and Waltham. Several minor differences between the two will be noted but their overall affinity is beyond doubt. Photographed by the bridge near the locomotive shed.

landowner where the locomotive was intended to work, leases for which were then (1902) in negotiation. The origin of the name THE SCOT has not been traced.

The next two locomotives were obtained to cope with the extra work demanded by the Branston extension. UNDERBANK was another four-wheeler obtained second-hand – a Peckett whose neatness of outline was marred by a stovepipe chimney until a new one was fitted in 1957. The other was a six-wheeler by Bagnall and very different from the typical contractor's locomotive, and evidently ideally suited for working the three-mile trip to Branston, for a similar locomotive was ordered in 1923. These two worked the bulk of the ore over the Eastwell main line, leaving the four-wheelers to do the purely quarry work, i.e. taking wagons from working face to main line loop.

All later locomotives came from other quarries. BANSHEE and WOODCOCK came from the closed Burton Latimer quarries, but did not do much work; BANSHEE was soon sent to Scaldwell and WOODCOCK ceased work about the end of World War II. The latter locomotive was one of the few Black Hawthorns in the ironstone fields and was typical of the maker's design with the rather square saddle tank, square spectacles, angularly cutaway cabsides, and brass nameplates with bold block letters. On withdrawal she was relegated to the loop on the disused Beech Grove branch, along with a number of the old-type wagons and was cut up in August 1948. The last two locomotives came from Stanton when their three-foot system at Harston was replaced by standard gauge – an Avonside six-coupled side tank and the squat and powerful-looking saddle tank supplied by Hunslet in 1936 and appropriately bearing the name BELVOIR. On arrival at Eastwell these two locomotives had their pairs of buffers removed and replaced by the centre buffing and drawgear standard at Eastwell. Shortly after their arrival THE SCOT was withdrawn from service and stored (greased up) in the open by the workshops at the top of the incline, but was later transferred to the 'exchange siding' by the Eaton branch, where she gradually fell to pieces and was finally cut up just before Christmas 1957.

The livery of the Staveley-built engines is not known but the Hudswell Clarkes, Bagnalls and Peckett UNDERBANK were all dark green lined red and yellow, with red coupling rods and red-backed nameplates of the makers' styles, whilst WOODCOCK had black lining as well; in the case of the Bagnalls, theirs would be the builders' standard livery, which was possibly adopted by the Eastwell company and applied to their

Eastwell Quarries. There was one secondhand Peckett, UNDERBANK, of typical outline. 30th June 1952. K. Cooper/IRS Collection

Eastwell Quarries. When the much longer extension to the Branston area was laid, two six-wheeled Bagnall locomotives were purchased. Shown is MOUNTAINEER, with a train of empties awaiting filling at Baulk face on 30th June 1952. Quarry machines are two 43RBs, a dragline and a shovel. K. Cooper/IRS Collection

Eastwell Quarries. WOODCOCK was supplied to Burton Ironstone Co Ltd. in Northamptonshire, and was named after the quarry manager there. She moved to Eastwell when the Burton quarries were closed – a Black Hawthorn, not many of which came to the ironstone fields. 20th June 1937. G. Alliez/courtesy B.D. Stoyel

Eastwell Quarries. BELVOIR was built for the Woolsthorpe quarries, like NANCY, and came to Eastwell in 1950. She shared the long-distance work with the Bagnalls.
L.W. Perkins

locomotives as they required repaint. After World War II lining was omitted and the engines turned out in plain green with red rods, MOUNTAINEER and PIONEER being the first so treated. LORD GRANBY and UNDERBANK were repainted in a paler green, which was also applied to BELVOIR shortly after acquisition. NANCY was plain green.

The locomotive shed was a long single-road building of red corrugated iron standing alongside the main line near the incline head and by it the familiar 'sausage' water tank on brick pillars; the repair shop lay in the junction between the main line and the branch to Beech Grove quarry, and held two locomotives.

Turning back to the inception of the Branston extension, we find from 1913 the expected intensification of activity, with quarrying continuing at Park, Newbridge and some other faces in the Eastwell area as well as adjoining the extension. On the latter, three faces were opened up, but two of them were only short-lived, one on each side of the river Devon in the small area between the Eaton branch and the Waltham road; the stone here was not of good quality, it also appears. The other working was the West Branston quarry a half mile south-east of Eaton; this face was worked up to 1932, but other faces further east towards Branston, collectively referred to as Branston quarry, were developed continually up to 1951, with the main tramway extended as required. Another face, further west and south of the tramway, was opened in 1947 and worked for 10 years; this was the Compressor pit, so titled from the compressor (an hydraulic pump near Eaton Grange) in the field close by. A new lease was secured from Belvoir Estates Ltd. for 32 years from 29th September 1936 and comprised 931 acres in the parishes of Eaton, Branston and Eastwell.

The older quarries on the western side were becoming exhausted, and working ceased at Dairy Farm in 1912, Park in 1918 (reopened on 8th November 1943), Newbridge on 11th August 1938 and Beech Grove on 16th October 1940. At Park quarry on 26th February 1953 a hoard of two thousand Roman coins was found when an excavator smashed the pot wherein they were contained; the pot was restored by B.P. Abbott. There were other Roman relics – beads, vases, metalwork etc.; Mr Coy kept some items, including a vase the size of a carboy, at his home, but these will eventually join the rest of the collection in Leicester Museum. Another quarry, between Park and the Eastwell-Scalford road, had been in production since the middle 1890s, and latterly was known as the

Eastwell Quarries. The other locomotive from Woolsthorpe was the Avonside side tank, NANCY. This photograph, taken on a very hot day in July 1952, shows the locomotive with the cab backplate removed. Ken Cooper/IRS Collection

Eastwell Quarries. View from the overbridge, looking towards the quarries. On the left is the workshops, with UNDERBANK outside; on the right is the locomotive shed, with one of the Bagnalls and BELVOIR in steam. 29th March 1956. J.R. Bonser

Coronation pit; in World War II some ground near the road was worked over a second time at a deeper level, until the pit was closed on 6th November 1943. The name of the quarry was current in 1939, as it is mentioned in LI, but we are not sure *which* coronation is commemorated by the title!

As the ironstone at outcrop or under shallow cover was exhausted machinery was introduced; this was particularly the case on the Branston extension, where the overburden went up to 30 feet, and the hard stone was blasted and then loaded by navvy. However, Eli Coy remembers a steam digger at work in Beech Grove quarry when he started work at Eastwell in 1918, and the identity of this machine has been confirmed by George Kemp. Three 20-ton Ruston steam navvies were purchased during World War I, one of them a long-jib shovel as new, while another was converted in 1931 for use in conjunction with a transporter new from Ruston Bucyrus. One of the steam diggers may have worked in Park or Coronation pits. In 1937 came the first new diesel dragline and from then onwards the steam machines were gradually replaced by diesel counterparts, all by Ruston Bucyrus – some new and some from other quarries. As the conditions were not too onerous (compared with some of the quarries in the Northampton Sand, for example), the machines were all of modest size, with nothing bigger than a 43RB. By the end of Word War II most of the steam machines were finished and the three diggers and a transporter were dumped in a row at the end of the Branston extension along with about 200 discarded small wagons.

In 1950 the Eastwell system was essentially the same as it had been for the past 30 years, and some of the operating methods went back for 70 years. Among the latter was the handling of wagons on the incline, typical of similar installations elsewhere. As a wagon reached the summit, it was unhooked from the rope and coupled to the one in front by a lad by the dexterous manipulation of two pointed sticks, the first wagon of the rake being 'spragged' by a steel bar with three spikes; at the foot of the incline for some reason, eight-sided wooden sprags were used for wagons waiting to be emptied. There were usually thirty wagons to a train, and thirty trains could be handled in seven hours. Mechanisation in the quarries affected the size of the workforce, which was about 300 in the days of full hand labour, but only 100 when fully mechanised; in the closing stages, with lorry operation, the number dropped to fifty.

The Eastwell incline was the last in the ironstone quarries and by 1950 Eastwell and Waltham were becoming anachronistic as the Stanton

Eastwell Quarries. Long jib Ruston shovel (442) working at one of the Branston quarries.
G. Rowley/Collection Greg Evans

Eastwell Quarries. Shovel RP 491 loading wagons, probably in one of the Branston quarries.
George Rowley, per Bert Smith

Eastwell Quarries. Three Ruston steam navvies out of use at Branston on 17th April 1957 RP526, 442, 491 from left to right. The track beyond led to the road running to Branston village but the proposed quarrying never took place. M.C. Fayers

Eastwell Quarries. The steam machines were replaced by diesels, and the photograph shows two 43RB machines, a dragline stripping and a shovel loading ironstone in Baulk pit. Ruston Bucyrus

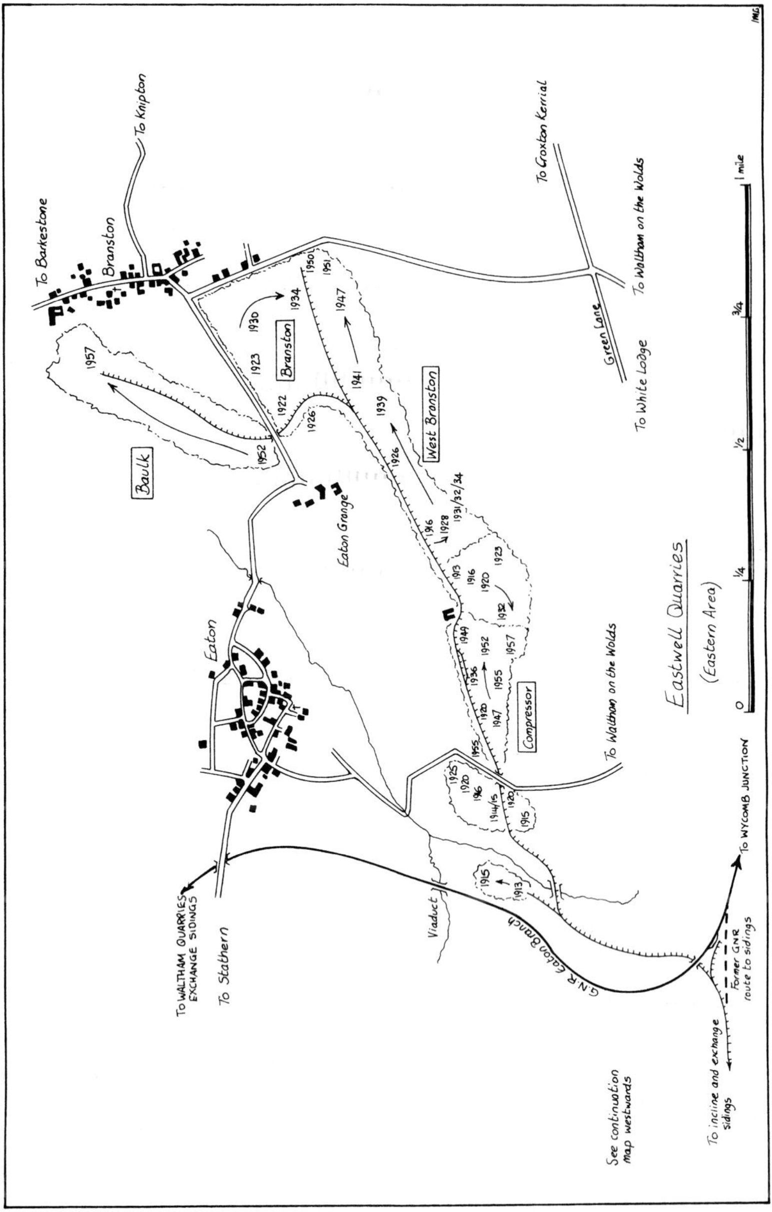
Eastwell Quarries
(Eastern Area)
0
1/4
1/2
3/4
1 mile
To Barkestone
Branston
To Knipton
To Croxton Kerrial
To Waltham on the Wolds
Green Lane
To White Lodge
Baulk
Branston
West Branston
Eaton Grange
Eaton
Compressor
To Waltham on the Wolds
To WYCOMB JUNCTION
Viaduct
G.N.R. Eaton Branch
To WALTHAM QUARRIES EXCHANGE SIDINGS
To Stathern
Former GNR route to sidings
To incline and exchange sidings
See continuation map westwards
1957
1952
1923
1930
1934
1922
1926
1950
1951
1947
1941
1939
1926
1931/32/34
1916
1928
1913
1916
1920
1923
1932
1957
1949
1952
1936
1955
1920
1947
1955
1925
1920
1916
1914/15
1920
1915
1915
1913

three-foot systems were closed; Eastwell took over two of their locomotives that, being six-wheelers, were of use to them. It is perhaps rather surprising to find tramway extensions still to come. At this time there were two quarries in production – Branston and Park – but in 1951 the branch to Beech Grove quarry, that had been dormant since 1941, was resleepered, extended and opened for traffic again. An unusual feature of the branch was a somersault signal of home-made fishtail pattern, probably because both branch and main lines were in cutting and the junction obscured. After about three years the branch was taken up completely, but the signal was left standing and eventually found its way to the Narrow Gauge Railway Museum at Towyn. At the other end of the system more important work was in hand, including two new bridges, one under the Eaton-Branston road and one under the Branston-Lings Hill road. These bridges were of superior construction, concrete lined beneath and the parapets of dressed blocks of ironstone that blended beautifully with the locale; it seems that this was the idea of Mr Ashwell, the engineer, and the blocks were quarried at Newbridge. The top row of blocks on the Eaton-Branston road bridge were smooth and semi-circular, while the Lings Hill road bridge had a series of parallel rough pointed stones. Both were built in 1951/52 and in the latter year quarrying commenced north of the Eaton-Branston road bridge at what was called 'Baulk face'; but no quarrying was ever done beyond the Lings Hill road bridge, which in fact was never cleared out completely beneath; it lay 3 ¼ miles from the top of the incline. The line between it and the main tramway was used as a dumping ground for surplus equipment, as already stated, until July 1957, when a new temporary line was laid along the same cutting to facilitate removal of the scrap.

In this year quarrying ceased at Branston, and with it long-distance haulage on the Eastwell system, for which 1957 was the critical year. There were still plenty of reserves, but much of the equipment was old and outdated, and on the tramway only two locomotives were workable. Conversion of the line to standard gauge, connecting with the Eaton branch, was considered, but costs were regarded as prohibitive, and the narrow gauge was allowed to continue. A new face of Coronation quarry, separated from the old face by a 'washout' was in production from June 1956, served by a branch from the main tramway close to the Eastwell-Scalford road. The locomotives had to run up as far as the wooden water tank just beyond White Lodge to refill their tanks, however, as the water at the shed was only fit for washing-out purposes; the practice ceased on

Eastwell Quarries. The trackbed of the route to Beech Grove quarry on the escarpment, with the signal protecting the approach to the 'main line' by the workshops (behind camera). 21st April 1958. H.C. Casserley

Eastwell Quarries. View looking east of the well-built bridge with parapets of dressed ironstone blocks on the road running north from Branston village. Quarrying was planned on this side of the bridge but never took place and for many years 2ft gauge tramway equipment was stored under the bridge. Regrettably the bridge was filled in and the parapets were replaced by wire fences; but the stone was used for repairing churches etc. 11th May 1976. Eric Tonks

Eastwell Quarries. AEC tipping lorry No. 2 at the loading dock at Stathern Sidings, March 1960.
D.H. Newman

Eastwell Quarries. Lorry loading, probably in No 5 quarry, 5th November 1965. BSC

the provision of a new tank by the Scalford road at about the end of 1958, and the section of line from the quarry junction to White Lodge rapidly assumed the rusty and neglected air that had already overtaken the further extensions. The track by White Lodge overbridge was cut by removing a rail.

Locomotives PIONEER and NANCY worked the traffic throughout the remaining life of the tramway; LORD GRANBY was taken into the workshops in 1958 and repairs commenced but not completed, and MOUNTAINEER was also taken into the shop in June 1959, but no work was done on her. The other two engines, BELVOIR and UNDERBANK, which had done no work for some time, were moved about the premises until finally displaced from their rightful resting place by a lorry, when they were left in the open by the workshops. The successful use of standard gauge at their Mill Hill quarry caused the company to consider afresh its installation at Eastwell. The new exchange point involved a longer mileage to Staveley Works, and BR asked for an extra two shillings per ton on the freight charge; and by the time BR had reconsidered and reduced the charge by one shilling, the decision had been taken to utilise the existing despatch point with lorry haulage between it and the quarries. A road for lorries across the field from the Eastwell-Harby road to a new tipping dock alongside the wagon tippler was completed in September 1959; the 'new' dock was in fact on the site of the long-disused dock designed for the smaller tubs, with the brick footings concreted over. The first AEC lorry (877 FAU) arrived later that month and the second (458 FTV) on 20th October. The tramway was then closed for regular use the following day, when Mr Coy, the manager, drove PIONEER into the yard for the last time.

The Day Book for Wednesday 21st October 1959 records the event simply as the 'last day of steam', but it was of some significance to the men who had spent a lifetime with the quarries and therefore the tramway, and the locomotives were covered with chalked inscriptions – 'Last Train E.I.O. Co 1959' on the rear of NANCY; 'My Life Is At Its End' on the side of PIONEER, and others. In the cab of NANCY appeared the following notice:

'Instructions for future use:

(1) Put water in boiler.
(2) Sticks and coal in firebox.
(3) Light fire.
(4) And await substance known in 1959 as STEAM.'

Thenceforward the tramway was only to be used a reluctant deputy, but it was decided to keep it intact for the winter in case the lorries had difficulty on the hills – in icy weather, for example. Two lines of loaded tubs were stationed at the top of the incline, which had its usual complement dotted all the way down, so that output could be maintained at a moment's notice. In the event, no trouble arose with the new arrangements, and on 10th August the decision was taken to dispense with the tramway. On 15th August NANCY was steamed (PIONEER was to have been used, but was found to have leaky tubes) to marshal the stock in the yard preparatory to clearing the incline and the remaining tubs of ore (some already sprouting weeds) on the following day. The whole proceedings on the 16th were filmed by Mr W.A. Camwell, ensuring a permanent record of an historic event – the passing of the last rope-worked ironstone incline in this country. The full tubs were lowered down the incline in the usual way, with empties coming off at the top alongside. At 2.30 p.m. the last full wagon was attached to the cable by Mr Coy. A garland of wild flowers – freshly picked marjoram and hawkweed from the cutting – was placed on the loaded ore, and the inscription 'LAST TRAM 16/8/60. Running 1880-1960' chalked on the side of the tub. With no more full wagons going down, empties were detached at the bottom, the last dozen or so being 'spragged' and then pushed on to the tippler by hand. At 3.20 the last tub was emptied into the BR wagon below and the incline was clear of wagons – a strange sight and, as Mr Coy put it, 'the end of an era'.

Meanwhile, at the summit, NANCY was dispersing from the incline top the empty tubs that were then hauled by a lorry on to the grass verge to await cutting up. The locomotives, which had been put out of the shed whilst these operations were going on, were marshalled in a line extending from the cable house to the bridge – UNDERBANK, LORD GRANBY, MOUNTAINEER, PIONEER and BELVOIR. On the 28th NANCY came out of her lonely shed again, this time to give a farewell trip over the usable portion of the line for the benefit of Birmingham Locomotive Club members, who turned up nearly a hundred strong. A convoy of cars and motor-cycles collected, such as had never been seen before at Eastwell. A horde of amateur photographers swarmed round the decaying stock until recalled to the waiting train by a prolonged toot on NANCY'S deep-toned whistle. The train was propelled to the quarry for more photography, and then NANCY, suitably inscribed 'Good-bye' in chalk, went back again without a slip, snorting under the bridge below a battery of cameras, to the yard. Here NANCY went on shed to drop her fire for the last time and then rejoined her confreres in the open, for the benefit of the photographers. Removable plates were taken off for safe-keeping.

Eastwell Quarries. The IRS enjoyed a farewell tour of the tramway on 28th August 1960, with the 'passengers' travelling in ironstone tubs hauled by NANCY. This view is at the entrance to Coronation pit. Vera and Vivienne (and a little of Rosalind!) Tonks on the first wagon. M.C. Fayers

Three months later Ken Cooper described the system 'This was a farewell visit by me to the two narrow gauge systems and my final photographs at Eastwell were taken when the rays of the late afternoon November sun were almost horizontal, and lighting the general scene with a strange brilliance against an eastern sky of gathering gloom'. Towards the end of the year track-lifting commenced, using road vehicles, and by Christmas had extended from the yard to White Lodge. 200 tons of rail went to the Tal-y-Llyn Railway, and some went to Middlesbrough. The incline was still intact, and so were the 'trams' at the top and foot. Eric Burroughs of Ketton ('Eric the Burner') arrived from his work at Waltham in January 1961, and commenced operations on the wagons at the incline foot before attending to the stock at the top.

By this time, narrow gauge locomotives were increasingly in demand for preservation both by established museums and by private individuals; and by 1961 the earlier preference for two-foot gauge exhibits was giving way to a wider appreciation, which benefited the Eastwell stock. LORD

GRANBY was found promise of a home in Leeds Museum by the efforts of the Narrow Gauge Railway Society, to whom the company kindly donated her, with the brand-new smokebox door intended for THE SCOT but never used. On Friday, 21st April 1961 she was loaded on to a lorry and transported to the Copley Hill (Leeds) store for restoration and storage until moved to the Industrial Museum at Armley Mills, Leeds, in March 1980. It had been hoped to preserve NANCY at Belvoir Castle and, the Duke of Rutland having given the idea his sanction, we inspected, with the Duke's agent at the castle, a shed that would take her. Unfortunately, the brothers Stirland of Watnall had already offered to take her and did so on the afternoon of Tuesday, 3rd October 1961; she lay neglected in their yard for many years and then went to Shanes Castle in Ireland. One of the wagons, peculiar to the narrow gauge tramways of the Staveley group, was found a home (again at the Leeds Museum) by the Narrow Gauge Railway Society, who took it away on Sunday, 8th April 1962. A dragline had been brought from the pit and was used to lift the tub on to the 'pick-up', which had been fitted with boards to take the wheels. Going up the long hill to its new temporary home in Golcar, Mike Swift commented: 'We kept half an eye on the tram and tried to visualise its effect on the following bus, should it break away'. Towyn Museum also came in for some small items – Level Crossing notices; the branch signal post; a whistle, believed to be from THE SCOT; and a pair of ex-Belvoir tramway plates that had long been at Eastwell. We also lugged home a couple of sprags – one wood and one steel.

The rest of the tramway equipment went in 1961, with the exception of BELVOIR, which was kept as a possible reserve for Scaldwell quarries. UNDERBANK was cut up in February to make way for the removal of LORD GRANBY behind her, but after that Mr Burroughs concentrated on wagons, of which there were about 250 at the closure, and it was not until well into the summer that the two Bagnalls were scrapped, the exact dates being unrecorded. The wintry scene in January 1962 was a sad one for the railway enthusiast; about a hundred yards of track, BELVOIR rusting away with the smokebox door yawning open, and the solitary tub isolated in the empty yard beneath the office. The cuttings and embankment remained as before, sharply etched on the snow-mantled countryside. 'Eric the Burner' returned to Eastwell in the summer of 1962 and cut up BELVOIR, one nameplate and makers' plate being presented at a small ceremony by the Birmingham Locomotive Club to Belvoir Castle museum as a sort of consolation prize for the loss of NANCY. The cuttings were then being filled in and land restored to agriculture.

Near the end of 1961 a third lorry (939 KTV) arrived and a garage to hold all three was built in the following year; the lorries were numbered 1, 2, 3 and the garage wall in front of their stands was decorated with the name and makers' plates of MOUNTAINEER, PIONEER and UNDERBANK, later taken by Mr Coy to his home.

We have run ahead a little to describe the end of the tramway, a sad event to the railway enthusiast; but it was not the end of quarrying at Eastwell, and we will now go back to take up the tale. There had been a number of administrative changes over this period, with alterations to the company title, as listed at the head of this section; in addition, Stewarts & Lloyds Minerals Ltd took control from 12th September 1960, without affecting the title, but influencing policy. Mr Eli Coy remained as manager, and regarded the title Eastwell & Loddington Ironstone Co Ltd as a personal tribute to him! The second lorry arrived just before this change took place and carried the earlier title 'Eastwell & Waltham Ironstone Co Ltd.' on a sticker that could be removed to reveal 'Eastwell & Loddington Ironstone Co Ltd.' beneath. These lorries had an orange livery (Stewarts & Lloyds Minerals lorries were yellow) and carried ten tons as against sixty tons per train. The Branston area was not reopened and efforts were concentrated on the western portion, with the principal working at Coronation pit, to which a lorry exit was made to the Eastwell-Scalford road. This was a period of depression at the ironworks, and Coronation pit was closed on 2nd November 1963; working was transferred to Newbridge pit for two years up to 3rd April 1965, and finally to Dairy Farm pit for two more years. This was only on a small scale however and production at Dairy Farm ceased on 13th January 1967, with the last men paid off on 25th February 1967.

The main trackbed had been incorporated in to the adjacent fields soon after lifting of the rails but there were still a number of reminders of the tramway in the form of bridges, that exhibited quite a variety of styles:–

Brick with rough ironstone top – by office.
Brick with concrete top – Beech Grove quarry; Dairy Farm quarry; Eastwell-Scalford road.
Brick with concrete top, plus side pillars – Newbridge quarry.
Blue brick, Great Northern Railway style – White Lodge.
Dressed ironstone blocks with round top – Baulk quarry.
Dressed ironstone blocks with rough stone top – Branston.

Eastwell Quarries. The sheds to the right of the incline summit on 15th October 1988. Former workshops on left and shed for lorries at right, with diesel fuel tank. A.J. Cocklin

Eastwell Quarries. A group of IRS members inspecting the tipping dock alongside the former Joint line trackbed. The brick portion to the right was used by the tramway wagons, the concrete one on the left by lorries. BR trackbed in foreground. 15th October 1988. A.J. Cocklin

Most of the quarries (e.g. Coronation) were smoothed over and restored to agriculture, but some quarry sections were left with the final face visible, e.g. Newbridge, Dairy Farm, Compressor, Baulk, as reminders of past activity. The brick buildings remained at the headquarters – the workshops and lorry shed – as well as the wooden office. On 15th May 1971 we took a party of students from Leicester on a tour of inspection of quarry remains, and at Eastwell we were greeted by a former employee, Mr Rixon, with: 'I was sure you would come along some day – I've something for you' – a nameplate of THE SCOT and the maker's plate of NANTES, the latter of course unique. Hopes that the few remains might be left in perpetuity were dashed in 1976 by the closing-down activities of British Steel Corporation Tubes Division, North of the Welland, which included the effacement of quarrying as far as possible and the elimination of future BSC responsibility. With the exception of the GNR bridge by White Lodge, all bridges under roads were filled in and the parapets knocked down and replaced by fences of wire and wood, sometimes with a quickset hedge. The parapet brickwork was often used to fill in beneath, and stone from an ancient pit on the escarpment by Beech Grove was also used; Baulk bridge was filled in from the still open face alongside. The removal of these parapets was a shame; they would certainly have looked better and lasted longer than the flimsy wire and wood replacements, as well as giving a clue to bygone activity. This particularly applied to the beautiful bridges at Baulk and Branston – the stones from which were good enough to be taken up for the repair of churches built of the local stone.

Nevertheless, a few reminders are still here. The tipping dock walls – brick for the later wagon tippler, concrete for the lorries – stand, and the lorry road itself is still here. Looking up the hillside, one can see faint traces of the course of the incline to where it enters the trees; and it is best seen from here, as the portion within the trees is a noisome rubbish dump. The incline summit area boasts the original bridge, its arches blocked by sheets of corrugated iron, with the dilapidated office building alongside, while down the yard the workshop and lorry shed are in use for other purposes, and are in good condition. Some filling up of this area was begun in 1988. Nothing can be seen of the tramway route, levelled and marked by one replacement hedge. The quarry areas are crossed by replacement hedges in the main, but in the vicinity of the GNR bridge (still intact) is a former GNR wooden fence on the west side and on the east is a handsome walnut tree that has featured in a number of photographs

Eastwell Quarries. The GNR bridge provided a fine vantage point for the photographer, with the walnut tree making a nice centrepiece. Locomotive is BELVOIR. 27th September 1954. G. Alliez/courtesy B.D. Stoyel

taken from the bridge. Parts of the working faces remain at Newbridge and Dairy Farm. The Newbridge pit is worth a visit, as it exhibits the interesting geological feature of 'step-faulting'; in this the ironstone bed is broken up by a series of vertical splits, and the sections then pushed out of alignment, looking rather like a series of books on a partially filled shelf. It seems likely that the face was retained for this purpose, and certainly a path appears to have been beaten to it from the public footpath near White Lodge; unfortunately, while the ordinary section of the face is still clearly visible, the deeper step-faulted section was in 1980 so heavily overgrown as to be almost invisible even in winter, and certainly so in summer. En route to see this can be noted the sunken fields, often with a pool of water, of the Newbridge and Dairy Farm pits.

The tramway here was on the course of the former GNR Eastwell branch, as the widely-spaced hedges indicate, and, just beyond, the tramway passed beneath the Eaton branch by a bridge, now gone. Its course may be vaguely made out to the site of the former viaduct over the Devon, now filled in and crossed by a hedge. The course of the tramway can then be followed for most of its way by clues here and there all the way to the terminus, with portions of the face to be seen at the Compressor pit, and more substantial remains at Baulk pit. Imagination conjures up pictures of the little trains that used to run here, and which certainly graced the scene.

Footnotes

1. The first 300 tons of ore, transported by horse and cart to Harby & Stathern station, as recalled by 'Old Charlie' Shelton, probably refers to the trial loads.
2. Joint Committee Minutes, extracted by Geoffrey Webb.

Eastwell Quarries. An almost timeless scene from working days, as NANCY ambles across fields above the incline top, in the course of restoration, with a rake of wagons for the operating quarries. 15th April 1959.

R.M. Casserley

Grid References

759291	Tipping dock to Joint line
763287	Top of incline
766284	Locomotive shed/bridge
768286	Bridge to Beech Grove quarry
770279	Bridge under Melton-Scalford road
777278	Bridge to Newbridge quarry
783273	Bridge at White Lodge (GNR)
784272	Bridge to Dairy Farm quarry
767274	Egress for lorries from Coronation quarry
783280	Newbridge quarry face
783267	Southernmost working towards Goadby Marwood
791275	Exchange point with GNR branch
790271	Bridge under GNR branch
791284	GNR viaduct
792281	Bridge over stream
795283	Bridge under Waltham road
811290	Bridge under Branston road
806290	Bridge at Branston terminus
807284	Baulk pit terminus

Locomotives

Gauge: 3ft 0ins

JOHN GREEN	0-4-0STG	VC	Staveley		1884	8 x 12ins	2ft 9ins	New 1884	Scr 1913
BELVOIR	0-4-0STG	VC	Staveley		1885	8 x 12ins	2ft 9ins	New 1885	Scr c1920
LORD GRANBY	0-4-0ST	OC	HC	633	1902	11 x 16ins	2ft 6ins	New 10/1902	(1)
THE SCOT	0-4-0ST	OC	HC	776	1906	11 x 16ins	2ft 6ins	New 9/1906	Scr 12/1957
UNDERBANK	0-4-0ST	OC	P	873	1900	10 x 14ins	2ft 6½ins	(a)	(2)
BANSHEE	0-6-0ST	OC	MW	1276	1894	9 x 14ins	2ft 0ins	(b)	(3)
			Reb. MW		1910				
WOODCOCK	0-4-0ST	OC	BH	1046	1892	8 x 14ins	2ft 6ins	(c)	Scr 8/1948
			Reb. Staveley 1919						
PIONEER	0-6-0ST	OC	WB	1980	1913	13 x 18ins	2ft 9¼ins	New 11/1913	(4)
MOUNTAINEER	0-6-0ST	OC	WB	2203	1923	12 x 18ins	2ft 7¾ins	New 6/1923	(5)
SCALDWELL	0-6-0ST	OC	P	1316	1913	11 x 16ins	2ft 9ins	(d)	(6)
BELVOIR	0-6-0ST	OC	HE	1823	1936	12 x 18ins	3ft 0ins	(e)	(7)
NANCY	0-6-0T	OC	AE	1547	1908	10 x 16ins	2ft 6½ins	(e)	(8)

(a) ex Marple & Gillott Ltd, 1911; prev. Sheffield Corpn. Waterworks Dept.
(b) ex Burton Latimer Quarries c 1921
(c) ex Burton Latimer Quarries 1923
(d) ex Scaldwell Quarries c 8/1947
(e) ex Stewarts & Lloyds Minerals Ltd, Woolsthorpe Quarries, 8/1950

(1) to Leeds City Museum, Copley Hill store, 4/1961
(2) Scr to Eric Burroughs 2/1961
(3) to Scaldwell Quarries by 1928
(4) Scr by Eric Burroughs c 8/1961
(5) Scr by Eric Burroughs c 6/1961
(6) to Scaldwell Quarries 8/1950
(7) Scr by Eric Burroughs 8/1962
(8) to Stirland Bros, Watnall, Nottinghamshire 10/1961

Gauge: 2ft 0ins (constructional line)

KEIGHLEY	0-4-0T	OC	OK	2484	1908	(a)	(1)

(a) ex E. J. McKay, Keighley Sewage Works c 1912 (1) to Pilton Quarries c 1919

Quarry machines

No. 20	S. Navvy. Special	RP	442	1915			New 11/1915 (a)	(1)
No. 20	S. Shovel. Rail.	RP	491	1917	2¾ Cu. Yds.	26ft.	New 1917	(2)
No. 20	S. Navvy. Long jib.	RH	526	1918	1¼ Cu. Yds.	52ft.	New 11/1918	(3)
No. 5A	Transporter	RH	1683	1930			New 8/1930	(4)
43RB	D. Dragline	RB	3442	1937	1 Cu. Yd.	60ft.	New 8/1937	(5)
43RB	D. Shovel	RB	3799	1938	1¾ Cu. Yds.	27ft.	New 9/1938	(6)
33RB	D. Shovel	RB	8016	1943	1½ Cu. Yds.	21ft.	New 1943	(7)
37RB	D. Shovel	RB	6564	1941	1½ Cu. Yds.	45ft.	(b)	(8)
24RB	D. Dragline	RB	4951	1940	1½ Cu. yds.	60ft.	(c)	(9)
21RB	D. Shovel	RB	2999	1936	¾ Cu. Yd.	18ft. 6ins	(d)	(10)

(a) Converted in 1931 for use with transporter, with 2 ¼ Cu. yds, 37ft. 6ins.
(b) ex Sir Lindsay Parkinson Ltd, opencast coal site, Atherstone, Warwickshire, 1947. (at Charwelton Quarries to 1944)
(c) ex Park Gate Iron & Steel Co Ltd, Sproxton Quarries 10/1958
(d) ex Waltham Quarries c 1958

(1) in Branston quarries. Scr c. 1958
(2) probably in Branston quarries. Scr c. 1958
(3) New to Beech Grove quarry. Later to Branston quarries. Scr c. 1958
(4) New to Branston quarries. Scr 1958
(5) New to Branston quarries; to Baulk face. At Park quarry 1954. To Sproxton Quarries 7/1959; ex Sproxton 1/1961. To Sproxton 10/1961
(6) New to Branston quarries; to Baulk face; at Park quarry 1954. To Eaton Basic Quarries c 1965
(7) at Baulk face 1954; at New Bridge pit 1964/5. Scr by F. Cowman Ltd, probably at New Bridge
(8) at Baulk face 1954; at Coronation pit 1962; at Dairy Farm pit 1966/7. To Staffordshire Public Works Co. Ltd. 7/1967
(9) in Coronation pit. To Eaton Quarries c 1967
(10) in Coronation pit. To Sproxton Quarries 5/1959; ex Sproxton 1/1961. To Sproxton 10/1961; ex Sproxton c. 1965. Scr probably at Newbridge pit.

WOOLSTHORPE QUARRIES

Stanton Ironworks Co Ltd developed the Woolsthorpe quarries in much the same way as their quarries at Eaton, with a number of tramways, both narrow and standard gauge. The situation at Woolsthorpe was slightly different in that the larger area extended over three parishes in two counties; but to Stanton and their successors the quarries have always been collectively known as 'Woolsthorpe Quarries', after the site of the earliest workings at Woolsthorpe-by-Belvoir in Lincolnshire. Several tramways were involved but whereas three of the Eaton tramways survived to 1935, only one of the Woolsthorpe set did so; so it is not surprising to hear this system commonly referred to by industrial railway enthusiasts as 'Harston Quarries'. We shall adopt here the treatment used to describe the Eaton systems, by grouping all the workings under the heading 'Woolsthorpe' and then describing the tramways individually. In this way the development of the quarries will be seen in a logical sequence. Fortunately for us, we have Hewlett's 'The Quarries' to guide us, and – thanks to the longevity of some of the quarrymen (in general a long-lived breed, it seems) – a fair amount of information has been preserved.

WOOLSTHORPE (BREWER'S GRAVE) QUARRIES

Narrow Gauge Tramway
Owners: Stanton Ironworks Co Ltd

Woolsthorpe-by-Belvoir is a pretty village of one street at the foot of the Marlstone escarpment, on which stands Belvoir Castle; and it must not be confused with Woolsthorpe-by-Colsterworth, a mere nine crow-flying miles away. The ironstone lies on the high ground at the top of the escarpment as at Eaton and Eastwell and appears under very shallow cover over a wide area of plateau about a mile square and with a slight south and southeast dip. Stanton Ironworks Co Ltd sank trial pits here about 1879 and samples were conveyed by cart to the Grantham-Nottingham canal for transit to the ironworks. Following the success of the trials, the company obtained a lease dated 14th April 1883 to work ironstone on the estate of the Duke of Rutland (of Belvoir Castle) and also one of 1883 from Sir W.E. Welby Gregory of Denton Manor. Meanwhile, the Great Northern Railway was constructing its Belvoir (or Denton) branch, running almost south from Belvoir Junction on the Grantham-Nottingham lane, over the canal and then turning east to skirt the Marlstone Cliff in the vicinity of Cliff Wood. A siding, known for some obscure reason as Bottesford Siding, was put in here and a three-foot gauge cable-operated incline was laid through the wood to a tipping stage over the siding.

The earliest quarries were established at Brewer's Grave where Belvoir Road (Denton to Woolsthorpe) crosses the ancient trackway generally spoken of as Green Lane; south of the crossing it is a section of 'Sewstern Lane' and north is called 'Longmoor Lane'. Sewstern Lane was last commercially used by cattle drovers taking their animals to London, and today is a quiet backwater that for those on foot offers an attractive route between Woolsthorpe and Buckminster quarries; another name by which it is known is 'The Drift'. Working commenced north of Brewer's Grave in the angle between Belvoir Road and Longmoor Lane, and including about three hundred yards of the latter, on the Rutland lease, and Hewlett records that the first load of ore was despatched from Bottesford siding on 3rd August 1883 and taken down to Belvoir Junction by the contractor's locomotive, as the branch was not then completed – in fact it was not finished until 1884. The locomotive concerned was a Neilston saddle tank that was purchased by the Stanton company, becoming STANTON No. 8; later she was to return for another spell of duty at Harston.

The double-track incline, one third of a mile at about 1 in 12, lay entirely in the shady confines of Cliff Wood, and on the fringe of the latter at the summit were built a locomotive shed, workshops, etc, beyond which the line struck out half a mile across open fields to Brewer's Grave. A public footpath was carried over the tramway by a (probably) wooden bridge, the tramway being in shallow cutting at this point. The upper portion of the tramway was at first worked by horses, but in November 1883 a locomotive was transferred hither from Wartnaby and Mr E. Barber (of whom more anon) was sent from Finedon Hill to take charge of it. The locomotive displaced some horses[1] but not all, as Mr Job. Masson joined the company's employ as a horse driver at Brewer's Grave in 1884[2]; the animals were probably returned later when more steam motive power was obtained.

The locomotives known to have worked on this tramway are given below, but as the official records do not discriminate between Brewer's Grave and Harston, reliance has to be placed on the memories of old

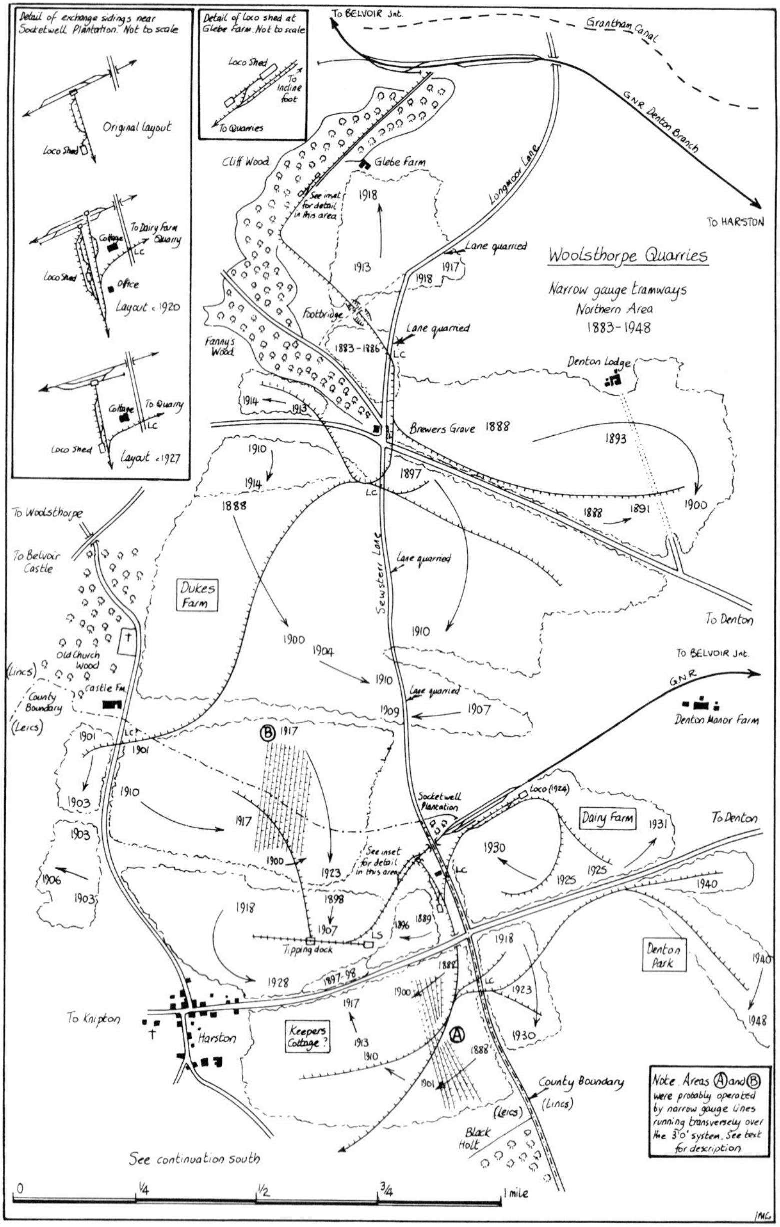
Woolsthorpe Quarries
Narrow gauge tramways
Northern Area
1883-1948
Detail of exchange sidings near Socketwell Plantation. Not to scale
Original layout
Layout c 1920
Layout c 1927
Detail of Loco shed at Glebe Farm. Not to scale
To BELVOIR Jnt.
Grantham Canal
GNR Denton Branch
To HARSTON
Cliff Wood
Glebe Farm
Longmoor Lane
Lane quarried
Fanny's Wood
Footbridge
Denton Lodge
Brewers Grave
Sewstern Lane
To Woolsthorpe
To Belvoir Castle
Dukes Farm
Old Church Wood
Castle Fm
County Boundary
To Denton
Denton Manor Farm
Socketwell Plantation
Dairy Farm
Tipping dock
Denton Park
To Knipton
Harston
Keepers Cottage?
Black Holt
Note. Areas A and B were probably operated by narrow gauge lines running transversely over the 3'0" system. See text for description
See continuation south
0 1/4 1/2 3/4 1 mile

employees. Fortunately, while Mr E. Barber was charge at Brewer's Grave, an almost equally long-lived gentleman, Mr Fred King, worked at Harston, and from their two recollections, supplemented by discussion with others, it has been possible to arrive at a fair approximation of the changing locomotive position of the earlier days. STANTON No. 11 was delivered new to Brewer's Grace, and a few years later the Fowler was despatched to Harston when the latter tramway was sufficiently advanced to require a locomotive; all traffic was then handled by No. 11 until STANTON No. 12 arrived in 1894 after a few weeks only at Harston. The stock remained at two – the capacity of the shed – until the last few years of operation, when NANCY was the sole occupant of the Cliff Wood shed. NANCY came new to Brewer's Grave but was delivered to the Denton Branch terminus near Harston, it being easier to take her thence by road than to haul her up the incline. In Stanton's records she is referred to as STANTON No. 18, but this was merely a book number, nameplates NANCY being carried when she was delivered by the makers. Wagons were of wood, probably generally similar in construction to those at Wartnaby, equipped for clipping to the cable of the incline, which was of the common double-acting or funicular type, with a tipping stage at the foot; the stage was carried obliquely over the railway siding, and from this the contents of the wagons were transferred to railway wagons below, probably by shovelling rather than by tipping.

Apart from the occasional exchange of a locomotive, there can have been little to vary the day-to-day tedium of the quarrymen's lot in the 35 years that the system was in operation. The initial workings by Longmoor Lane were exhausted in rather less than three years, and operations began at two much larger quarries. One lay east of Brewer's Grave, on the north side of Belvoir Road, and working was carried out in a roughly clockwise direction from 1886 to 1899, the furthest point reached lying about half a mile from Brewer's Grave. The other quarry was west of Sewstern Lane and, commencing in 1888, worked anticlockwise towards the latter, again reaching about half a mile from Brewer's Grave. The area between Belvoir Road and Sewstern Lane was commenced in 1897, working clockwise towards Sewstern Lane. These last two quarries both reached Sewstern Lane in 1909, when the lane was closed or diverted while the underlying stone was removed, and the lane then returned to its original site and an avenue of chestnuts was planted along each side. The quarry west of Sewstern Lane was in Woolsthorpe parish and was known as Duke's pit. The other two quarries were in Denton parish but the local names appear to have escaped record. There may have been an extension of the tramway west of the Woolsthorpe-Harston road south of Castle farm – see next section.

This major area was worked out by 1910 and later operations were on a smaller scale at three pits further north; two were south and north of the drive to Belvoir Castle from the lodge at Brewer's Grave, respectively worked in 1910-14 and 1913/4, and there was a larger area between the locomotive shed and Longmoor Lane, worked 1913-18. This was the last quarry to be served by the Brewer's Grave tramway and the incline was last used in the summer of 1918. Hewlett records that in its lifetime at least two thirds of the ironstone north of the Denton-Harston road was carried over the line, and that the only stone remaining in Woolsthorpe parish was a small area near the county boundary. With the stone so near the surface,no quarry machinery was ever used, all the operations being by hand. On closure, the tramway was dismantled and NANCY and serviceable wagons transferred away, the former to work the remaining stone in Woolsthorpe over another tramway (see below) and the latter either to the same tramway or to Harston.

When IRTM was published, the Brewer's Grave tramway was already a memory only to elderly employees, whilst the Harston quarries were still fully active. Today, Harston has followed Brewer's Grave into history, leaving very few traces behind; but the industrial archaeologist will find something to see at Cliff Wood, where the course of the incline is still very clearly defined, mostly in shallow cutting but near the bottom appearing on a slight embankment. By the tipping dock site at Bottesford Siding there is some brickwork suggestive of a narrow gauge siding parallel to the GNR line; the OS map shows the narrow gauge line going over the siding at an oblique angle, presumably for transfer of ore, but there may have been a siding as well – perhaps for the transfer of coal and other materials to be taken *up* the incline. At the top the locomotive shed and its ancillary building have completely disappeared, though some brickwork of the former was still visible in the 1950s. Of the course of the tramway over the fields there is no trace at all, and of the quarries the only noteworthy evidence is provided by Green Lane, that shows a distinct drop at each end of the section south of Brewer's Grave where the underlying stone was removed. The hedges were replaced by pure hawthorn with equally-spaced chestnut trees – very beautiful indeed. One can only muse and visualise the little engines jogging across the fields towards Cliff Wood; they would have looked lovely and by no stretch of the imagination a disfigurement of the landscape, which has suffered hardly at all. Woolsthorpe today is still the charming village of a century ago, sheltered by the greenery of the Cliff and unimpaired by the demands of the Iron Age.

Mention has been made of Ted Barber, whom we were bound to meet sooner or later; one could not seek historical information on Stanton's quarries without being referred to Ted Barber, who was one of the outstanding personalities of the ironstone industry – "The grand old man of the quarries" as he is described in 'The Stantonian' for July 1946, p.13. Edwin 'Ted' Barber was born in 1863 and in August 1874 entered the service of the Stanton Ironworks Co. at their colliery at Dale, known as Dale Open Hole, and three years later took charge of the winding engine there until the mine was closed in about 1878, when he was transferred to the ironworks. His health suffered however and, after he had had a recuperative holiday, the company sent him to Desborough ironstone quarries, where he worked with his father, who had been there since 1878. Ted then had a short spell at Wellingborough, operating the hauling engine of the Finedon Hill quarries, but in November 1883 had his last transfer, to Woolsthorpe to take charge of the locomotive just transferred from Wartnaby and of those that were to follow very soon; at Woolsthorpe "I have remained happy in this beautiful district". A photograph in his possession showed him on the footplate of one of his charges. Long after Ted had retired, his son Arthur, a mere lad of sixty odd, was in charge at Woolsthorpe, up to 1958.

We preserve happy memories of an interview we were privileged to have with this grand old gentleman, which he was in every sense; modest in ambition and temperament, he was remembered with affection by all his colleagues at Stanton, subordinate and superior, and at the age of ninety retained a bright eye, a lively recollection and a fund of memories and experiences of times and events now beyond recall. He remembered well the hard working conditions of his early years, when it was a commonplace for a quarryman to walk two or three miles to begin a day's toil commencing at 6.am, with the corresponding mileage home, wet or fine; and if heavy rain set in during the day, work would have to be abandoned and the meagre pay forfeited. Every tub was loaded by hand with ore loosened by the pick, and baring (removal of overburden) was carried out by shovelling the soil into barrows that were then trundled along planks supported on wooden trestles to the far side of the cutting for disposal; negotiation of a long narrow plank supported only at the

Woolsthorpe Quarries. Of the purely surface quarries at Brewers Grave and of the tramway serving them almost nothing can now be seen, but the incline through Cliff Wood is still readily traceable. This view was taken on 26th April 1976, about half way up. Eric Tonks

Woolsthorpe Quarries. 'The grand old man of the quarries', Ted Barber outside his home in Woolsthorpe on 28th March 1953.- his 90th birthday. E. Barber

ends was not without its hazards, too. Those days are gone forever and quarrying became a much mechanised business; but the engine driver did not perhaps change so much. Transfers between neighbouring tramway systems was usually carried out by road by the time-honoured method of laying a short length of rail track to carry the engine, and taking up the rear portion and placing it in front of the advancing locomotive; tedious,and with an element of excitement on hills and of course not to be seen again.

Footnotes

1. 'The Stantonian', September 1946, p.13
2. Ibid, 1930, p. 141

Harston Quarries south of the Denton-Harston road: Narrow Gauge Tramway
Owners: Stanton Ironworks Co Ltd.

The Great Northern Railway Belvoir branch, opened to Bottesford Siding in 1884, was extended in the following year in a rough semicircle round the shoulder of higher ground to a terminus just west of Green Lane, that from this point to the Rutland border twelve miles to the south forms the boundary between Lincolnshire and Leicestershire. In railway company records this was termed the Denton branch – appropriately enough as the extension was almost wholly in Denton parish, Lincolnshire but for thirty years the workings from this terminus were in Leicestershire. In 1886 a gullet was opened up between the railway and the Denton-Harston road, the ore being carted to the GNR line; as soon as there was enough space, a three-foot gauge tramway was laid from a tipping stage on the south side of the railway and in 1887 a tunnel was made under the road,and operations commenced on the south.

The workings north of the road, west of Green Lane, from 1887 to about 1896, were clockwise and only on a small scale, with a line direct to the tipping stage, and may well have been worked by hand. South of the road the initial transport arrangements seem to have been rather unusual, judging from the survey plans; the tramway curved westwards south of the bridge and the ground was quarried in strips a third of a mile in length and running roughly north-north-west to south-south-east, i.e. almost at right angles to the tramway. R.F. Percy[1] describes a unique form of tram (tub) used at Woolsthorpe; in this the frame of the wagon carried a body in two halves, joined at the top of the sides so that when tipping the bottom of the wagon divided across the centre into two parts to allow the ore to be discharged. It seems likely that these tubs were used here, running on a separate tramway, of unknown gauge,that was carried over the three-foot line, which was extended as working progressed westwards. In 1900 however a more orthodox system was adopted, with the three-foot line taken from the working face, that was advanced clockwise from the south towards the road, reached in 1917. A new locomotive was obtained from Bagnall's in 1900, evidently to work this new line, and two more came from Brewer's Grave in the next decade. The first locomotive also came from Brewer's Grave, probably in 1887 or soon afterwards, though the precise date is unknown; she would be sufficient for the limited locomotive work required up to 1900. It is

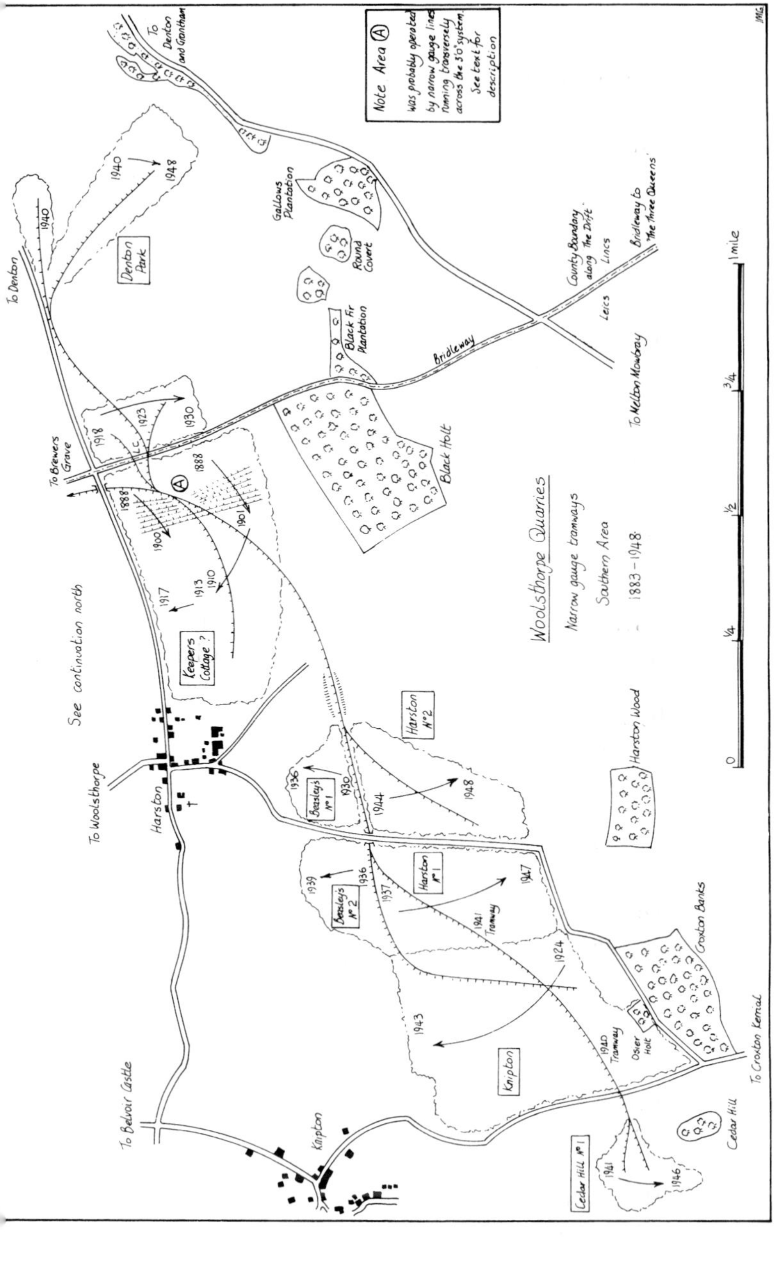
Woolsthorpe Quarries
Narrow gauge tramways
Southern Area
1883 – 1948
Note Area Ⓐ
was probably operated by narrow gauge lines running transversely across the 3'0" system. See text for description
To Denton
To Denton and Grantham
Denton Park
Gallows Plantation
Round Covert
Black Fir Plantation
Bridleway
County Boundary along The Drift
Lincs
Leics
Bridleway to The Three Queens
To Melton Mowbray
Black Holt
To Brewers Grave
Keepers Cottage ?
See continuation north
To Woolsthorpe
Harston
Harston No 2
Harston No 1
Beasley's No 1
Beasley's No 2
Harston Wood
Croxton Banks
Osier Holt
To Croxton Kerrial
Knipton
Cedar Hill
Cedar Hill No 1
To Belvoir Castle
Tramway
0
1/4
1/2
3/4
1 mile

believed that the southern quarries were known as Keeper's Cottage quarries.

The rail layout was at first very simple, with a loop by the tipping stage and a small locomotive shed, but later -the year is unknown – the shed was extended, with a bend in the middle, to hold three locomotives. It was a single line brick structure with a corrugated iron roof; the windows were iron-framed with semicircular tops but on the east side these were later replaced by a modified design with only slightly curved tops. Behind the shed was a machine shop, and there was a storeroom and an office of brick nearby. In 1913 there was built a row of five cottages for employees, and one was for many years occupied by Arthur Barber, the quarry manager. Rails were spiked direct to wooden sleepers on earth ballast. The ironstone from north and south of the Denton-Harston road differed in physical form and chemical composition, that from the north being a soft brown ore, that from the south a harder, more limey stone lighter in colour. The road was not an exact dividing line between these two forms, of course, but the trend to the more limey stone lay to the south.

To meet wartime demands, a limited area of Denton Park, south of the road but east of Green Lane, was opened up; the branch tramway was built from a facing junction and crossed Green Lane on the level, and working commenced in 1918 southwards from the roadside edge in a clockwise direction as far as Green Lane, reached in 1929. In the final cut, it seems that the hedge bordering Green Lane was removed, as the present hedge is an obvious replacement one at a lower level. The survey plans suggest that the level crossing was moved about 70 yards south in 1923, no doubt to ease the curve. In this pit the ore was of the brown decalcified variety as found north of the road. The Welby Estates lease was renewed for 60 years from 1st July 1933 to cover over 4000 acres in the parishes of Harston, Denton and Sproxton (the last served by the Harlaxton system).

A more interesting development of this period involved a lengthy extension of the three-foot line to the Knipton area; leases to work ironstone here had been granted by the Duke of Rutland in 1891, but had not been utilized, and were renewed in 1917. Work commenced in 1920, the tramway being taken in a roughly west-south-west direction and including an embankment ('the causeway') where it crossed low ground south of Harston village, and a tunnel under the Harston-Croxton Kerrial road. This tunnel was blasted out of the rockbed, with some stone blocks and bricks at the top supporting girders, and narrow gauge rail and wood

Woolsthorpe Quarries. Ruston long-jib machine working in Knipton pit.
Stanton Ironworks Co Ltd

formed a roof. On the road above the original hedge was retained but on each side was placed a green-painted fence of corrugated iron bent to form three sides of an octagon. Presumably this was to prevent smoke drifting across the road – even though the traffic here was only light. About 400 yards beyond the bridge the line crossed the parish boundary into Knipton parish, and working commenced here in 1924 (when the road tunnel was opened), the face extending to the Harston-Croxton Kerrial road at Croxton Banks, and then working clockwise to the Croxton Kerrial-Knipton road. This was at the foot of the Oolitic Cliff and because of the slight south to southeast dip in the Marlstone bed, the overburden here was about twenty feet deep, heavier than at any of the workings in the vicinity; to deal with this the 20-ton Ruston Proctor navvy that had been used for loading ironstone on the standard gauge tramway (see below) was brought over and fitted with a long jib in September 1926. To cope with the additional output, a second tipping stage was erected, probably about 1920, on the east side of the original one, and standing over a new GNR siding north of the running line (the original stage stood over a line south of the running line). The narrow gauge layout at the terminus was remodelled accordingly.

Working at Knipton quarry was not completed until 1943. For much of this period there was activity in Harston parish on the Welby lease, on both sides of the road between there and Croxton Kerrial. Beasley's No. 1 Quarry on the east side, and north of the tramway, was worked 1930 to 1936, and Beasley's No. 2 quarry on the west side was worked 1936 to 1939 followed by Harston No.1 quarry south of the tramway, 1937 to 1947, then Harston No. 2 quarry east of the road and south of the tramway, from 1944 onwards. Thus, the four quarries Beasley's Nos 1 and 2 and Harston Nos 1 and 2, were worked in an anticlockwise circle from the bridge under the road from Harston to Croxton Kerrial. The overburden in the southern quarries was shallow but the stone harder and more limey, and required blasting, for which a powder magazine was built near the causeway. Similar conditions appertained in Knipton pit from 1931 onwards, as working receded from the Oolitic Cliff. In 1931 a Ruston steam dragline was brought over from the Dairy Farm quarries (see below); this stripped the soil, then the overburden, depositing each separately on the strip from which the ironstone had been removed. This machine worked both Knipton and Beasley's pits, moving on its caterpillar tracks between the working faces as required The last quarry in this district was Cedar Hill No. 1, lying west of the Knipton-Croxton Kerrial road; and the tramway continuation to it crossed the road on the level, the quarry lying almost due north of the cedar-covered hillock. The tramway was laid across the almost completely worked-out Knipton quarry and crossed Harston No. 1 by the side of the latest 'cut'. This was in the latter part of 1940, and production at Cedar Hill No. 1 commenced in the following year and was maintained up to 1946.

We have departed from strict chronology in favour of serial reference to all the quarries associated with the westward extension of the tramway, which was in use from 1920 until the end of the narrow gauge. The tramway was not however static as far as equipment was concerned and in 1927, some forty years after installation, further improvements were made. The wooden tipping stages were dismantled and replaced by a steel structure and a rotary tippler on the site of the first stage. At first, wooden wagons were used, and, later, squarish steel tubs that were pushed one at a time into the tippler, inverted to release the load into a railway wagon, returned to the upright position and pulled out. The layout at the tippler was modified to suit. The Belvoir Estates lease was renewed for 25 years from 30th June 1944 for 1145 acres in Knipton, Harston and Croxton Kerrial parishes.

Woolsthorpe Quarries. A train of wagons arriving at Beasley's No.2 quarry, during the opening-up operations, 1934. Stanton Ironworks Co Ltd.

Woolsthorpe Quarries. Rotary tippler over the BR siding, for emptying narrow gauge wagons coming in from Harston quarries. October 1948. Eric Tonks

Operations then carried on without much further change until 1937, when another No. 10 steam dragline was obtained secondhand. Then, at the outbreak of World War II, history repeated itself and working in Denton Park was resumed, this time on a larger scale. The tramway was laid across Green Lane and about half a mile beyond, and working commenced from near the Harston-Denton road and in the vicinity of Denton Manor, that had by then been pulled down; possibly, at the time of the earlier working in Denton Park, the company was not allowed to work within sight of the Manor. The overburden to start with was shallow, but became deeper in later years as working moved south towards the main Grantham-Melton Mowbray road. The working face moved westwards. During the war years working was intensive and was pursued at Knipton, Harston Nos 1 and 2, and Denton Park quarries, and a number of quarry machines was obtained. These included a No 4 steam shovel in Knipton pit, later in Denton Park; and the first diesel machines, with a tendency towards larger sizes at the end of the war; and the first electric machine, a 55RB, which worked in Harston No. 2 quarry.

The locomotives were as varied as those at Eastwell and were remarkable for numerous changes of title. The first engine was a Fowler 0-4-2T with 7-inch cylinders, that had already seen service at Wartnaby and at Brewer's Grave, but which was adequate for the light work involved. In 1900 a new engine arrived from W.G. Bagnall Ltd, a four-coupled saddle tank of their familiar design; originally this was intended to be titled STANTON No. 13 in sequence with STANTON No. 12 of 1894, but superstitious fears caused the change to STANTON No. 14[2], which title, painted in white, was however replaced almost immediately by nameplates HARSTON supplied by the makers. HARSTON went to Rothwell Hill and was replaced by STANTON No. 11 from Brewer's Grave. Another Hudswell Clarke, STANTON No. 10, came next and, apart from a five-year spell at Wartnaby, remained at Harston until the end of the narrow gauge. She was later rechristened KNIPTON by means of brass nameplates; the old title was merely painted on the tank. The Fowler, STANTON No 9, was the black sheep of the Stanton fleet and evoked many threats from her driver – 'Go, you ---, go. You aint havin' any more sand'. She went to Stanton ironworks for scrap in 1912.

The opening up of Denton Park required a further locomotive and a secondhand Hudswell Clarke, appropriately named DENTON, was obtained from Wake of Darlington. NANCY, used at Duke's Farm pits, was moved to Harston quarries in 1923, and thence forward the pattern of the locomotive stock is known from Stanton records. 'Between the wars' the allocation averaged four, but exchanges with other quarries occurred from time to time; a solitary Manning Wardle came from Earls Barton, but was not kept long. One new engine was obtained from the Hunslet Engine Co; this was the last narrow gauge steam locomotive purchased by Stanton and was a burly six-coupled saddle tank giving the impression of a standard Hunslet type squashed into a narrow gauge frame. The Avonside Engine Co supplied most of Stanton's standard gauge locomotives between 1900 and 1921 and when Hunslet took over Avonside's assets, further engines of similar design were supplied. The purchase of the last two narrow gauge locomotives from Avonside and Hunslet is thus consistent with Stanton's policy of the time. During World War II the stock was augmented by the Peckett from Eaton and these five engines worked intensively in the national interest; the arrival of STANTON No. 12 after the end of hostilities was rather one of convenience, as Stanton's narrow gauge lines were then doomed, and Harston itself closed down in the summer of 1948.

NANCY and BELVOIR were unusual machines, but the other locomotives at Harston were typical products of their makers at the time. All the stock finished up substantially in the condition as built and a

Woolsthorpe Quarries. STANTON No. 12, a typical Hudswell Clarke 0-6-0ST at the Harston tipping stage. Like most of Stanton's locomotives, she has served at other quarries. 2nd September 1947. G. Alliez/courtesy B.D. Stoyel

comparison of the early and later Hudswell Clarkes is interesting. The veteran KNIPTON with its sixty years of active service to its credit looked neat, if rather old-fashioned, with its graceful tapering chimney, tall highly polished safety valve cover, neatly rounded and rivetted tank, and rectangular makers plates. The livery of the earlier locomotives (or some of them, at least) was a warm reddish brown lined with black and sometimes yellow, with red coupling rods, and HARSTON and STANTON No 11 finished their lives so painted; but, as at other quarries, locomotives acquired after 1900 all had essentially green liveries, the final six at Harston being painted as follows: KNIPTON and STANTON No. 12 – green lined black, edged white: HOLWELL No. 5 – green lined black edged with yellow; WELBY, NANCY and BELVOIR – plain green. All had red connecting rods and nameplates of polished brass, with red-backed lettering in the case of BELVOIR, black for the others. The titling of the engines is complicated by changes that have obscured the original scheme, which was to number all Stanton's locomotives in one chronological sequence irrespective of gauge or location. The isolation of the various narrow gauge systems led to the abandonment of this scheme in the closing years of the nineteenth century, and the numbers formerly carried by narrow gauge locomotives were applied to standard gauge machines at Stanton ironworks, though STANTON No 18 and 19 were issued later to narrow gauge locomotives in chronological sequence. STANTON No 18 was so called only on paper, plates NANCY being carried when the engine was delivered. The application of names then became normal practice, to new and some old engines. The earlier locomotives had the titles painted on the tanks but in later years these were replaced by brass plates, with the solitary exception of BOTTESFORD, as mentioned under Wartnaby quarries. When names were selected, these had some local significance either of place or person; WELBY, for example, referred to the landowning family at Denton Manor and not to the village near Holwell – its previous name of KITTY was that borne at Rothwell Hill, where all of the locomotives carried girl's names. DENTON became STANTON No. 9 on transfer to Tilton, a curious reversion of practice. The lettering on the plates was usually of thin, non-serif type, but KNIPTON had bolder lettering, and BELVOIR thicker non-serif characters of Hunslet's standard pattern, As new, NANCY had an open-back cab, but for most of its life she operated with a removable spectacle plate probably made by Stanton. The original parallel-sided chimney also seems to have been changed for one slightly coned: and at

Woolsthorpe Quarries. KNIPTON, basically similar to STANTON No. 12 but of an earlier design; and very neat with its tall chimney, brass safety valve cover and rivetted saddle tank. The cab has been enclosed at some time. 2nd September 1947.

G. Alliez/courtesy B.D. Stoyel

Woolsthorpe Quarries. WELBY was another locomotive, a four-wheeler, that had also seen service elsewhere. When photographed on 17th September 1949 she was standing on the foundations of the shed that was built to serve the Dairy Farm pits, but by then the sides of the building had been taken down.

H.Gray

some time the Avonside nameplates with serif letters were replaced by Hunslet plates with block lettering.

Soon after the war, plans were made to abolish the outmoded narrow gauge system and to replace it by a standard gauge tramway from an end-on junction with the Denton branch, which was in line with Stanton's policy for its ironstone quarries. Except for BELVOIR, all the locomotives were getting on in years and had been worked very hard during the war; apart from that, the standard gauge system had the advantages of requiring fewer men and also permitted the use of larger quarry machines. The displaced three-foot system was taken up completely but for a section in the immediate vicinity of the engine sheds, and the line connecting them. The six locomotives were stored – NANCY, KNIPTON and HOLWELL No. 5 in the Dairy Farm shed (see next section) and WELBY, STANTON No. 12 and BELVOIR in the old shed, and lay there for nearly two years. On the occasion of the Birmingham Locomotive Club's visit on 24th October 1948, HOLWELL No.5 was steamed for the last time to enable her and KNIPTON to be photographed outside the shed against an attractive background of ripe elderberries. NANCY and BELVOIR were sold for further work at Eastwell, while the remainder were cut up on site by T.W. Ward in May 1950. The older locomotive shed was retained as a workshop and stores, and the associated buildings continued in their normal functions. The Dairy Farm shed and tipping stage were dismantled,. The site of the bridge under the Harston-Denton road was still marked by a black wooden fence, but most other traces were obliterated by the new standard gauge system. The rotary tippler was also dismantled but the site was utilized later as a lorry tip.

Footnotes

1. R.F. Percy: "The Belvoir Iron Ore". Transactions of the Institution of Mining Engineers. Vol. 22, pp30-34. 1901/2.
2. In Stanton's official records, the locomotive is referred to as No. 4 but it does not seem to have borne this title.

Harston Quarries north of the Denton-Harston road : Narrow gauge and standard gauge tramways.
Owners: Stanton Ironworks Co. Ltd

Though the quarries north of the Denton-Harston road were smaller in area than those to the south, the transport operations were much more complex; the quarries on the south side were all served by branches of one narrow gauge tramway system, but there were at least four separate systems on the north side. Some of the quarries are not specifically mentioned by Hewlett so, without his guidance, we have to rely on the survey maps for indications of how things were managed; some guesswork is therefore inevitable, as the events are now beyond living memory.

As mentioned briefly in the previous section, a small area was worked west of the first tramway in the years 1888-96, probably by hand over a short tramway towards the tipping stage; then from 1898 ground about a quarter mile west of the Denton branch terminus was opened up and operated up to 1907, almost certainly by means of a branch of the three-foot tramway running over ground already worked out to the existing tipping stage, and quite likely with locomotive haulage.

During the same period a larger area west of the Harston-Woolsthorpe road was worked; this stretched due south from Castle Farm for nearly half a mile, half of this alongside the road until the latter turned southeast, and working took place in the years 1901-1906. Working was resumed here half a century later under the title of Harston Glebe quarry. The survey map gives the dates only at the edges of the worked-out area, but indicate that the ground was worked westwards in strips roughly north to south; but *how* it was worked is not recorded. Possibly horse and cart haulage was used to convey the ore to the narrow gauge line, the nearest of which would be the southwestern extension of the Woolsthorpe (Brewer's Grave) tramway, which at that time was only a short distance east of the road by Castle Farm; indeed, the survey map has a couple of rather intriguing dates – May 1901 and June 1901 – respectively east and west of the road immediately south of Castle Farm, suggesting the possibility of a tramway being extended over the road at this time and then running south to the Harston Glebe area. Another possibility suggested by the 1901 date is that the method of working in strips transverse to the three-foot tramway, that had been used between 1888 and 1900 south of the Denton-Harston road, was moved to Harston

Glebe, with the three-foot line extended across the road to collect ore from the double-bodied wagons. All this is pure conjecture that may be way off the truth; but when working east of the Harston-Woolsthorpe road was commenced in 1910 we are on rather surer ground, as the survey map shows clearly working in north-south strips, the face moving eastwards, up to 1917. In this case, the three foot tramway outlet would be an extension of the line to the Harston tipping stage that had been used up to 1907.

The system of operating in north-south strips, presumably by tramways transverse to the three foot line, came to an end in 1917, when entirely new transport arrangements were introduced, probably with increased wartime output in mind. There were two areas of stone to be dealt with, the southern one separated from the quarries just described by a belt of sterile ground (probably of the type referred to by quarrymen as a 'washout') and lying due west of the Denton branch terminus, from which a standard gauge extension was built in 1917. This was worked by a Stanton locomotive, for which a small shed was provided, and two locomotives, both old, were involved. The first was STANTON No. 8, a Neilson saddle tank that had run the first loads of ore down the unfinished Belvoir branch in 1883, and which Stanton had purchased from the contractor. Her successor was an unidentified Hudswell Clarke saddle tank that came from Buckminster and returned there, after the job was completed, in 1925. Working was expedited by the purchase of a 20-ton Ruston steam shovel, which was used to load the ore directly to railway trucks. Quarrying extended as far as the Harston-Woolsthorpe road, anticlockwise from north to south.

North of this standard gauge system lay the quarries previously described, and to work the eastward section of this area a three foot tramway was laid to a tipping stage over a standard gauge siding that was also used to service the Ruston navvy. Operations commenced in 1918, this time by the orthodox narrow gauge system, clockwise from north to east. Locomotive NANCY was sent here from Brewer's Grave, where work had ceased that year. The area abutted the old Woolsthorpe quarries – indeed, the area was partly in Woolsthorpe parish – and was a southward extension of the old Duke's (or Duke's Farm) pit operated by the Brewer's Grave tramway; it was exhausted by 1923, when the tramway was dismantled and the locomotive sent to Harston quarries south of the road.

The last area to be worked north of the Denton-Harston road 'between the wars' lay east of Green Lane, between the Denton branch and the road, and was known as Dairy Farm quarries. They were served by a three-foot tramway that started from a junction with the old Harston tramway near the locomotive shed, passed in front of the cottages, then alongside an eastward extension of Denton sidings; a narrow gauge siding was laid here and a new tipping stage. In 1924 the initial gullet was driven southwards to the road, quarrying thereafter being carried out simultaneously at two faces, east and west. A No. 10 steam dragline was obtained new from Ruston & Hornsby to strip off the shallow overburden and the ore was then loaded into V-shaped steel side-tipping wagons and taken to the tipping stage. A new corrugated iron single road shed capable of holding three locomotives was erected close to the stage, so that the Dairy Farm system was to all intents and purposes operated as an independent unit, though it was connected to the main Harston system. The Dairy Farm quarries were in Lincolnshire and the stone was of the soft dark red variety. The area was worked out by 1931 and the lines to the pit taken up, but the connecting line to the main tramway and the locomotive shed were left in position to house the enlarged stock, and remained in use to the end of the narrow gauge. The planks of the loading stage were also left in position, to rot away over the years. It is not known which locomotives worked at Dairy Farm, but the probable ones are STANTON No. 11, DENTON and STANTON No. 19, described under the section dealing with the quarries south of the road.

Woolsthorpe Quarries. In 1947/8 the narrow gauge tramway system serving the Harston group of quarries was replaced by one of standard gauge making an end-on connection with the Denton branch. The photograph shows the new track approaching the north side of the new bridge under the road to Harston. A train may be seen approaching the bridge. Weigh house on right. June 1948. BSC

Harston Quarries south of the Denton-Harston road: Standard gauge tramway
Owners: Stanton Ironworks Co Ltd: Stewarts & Lloyds Minerals Ltd from 1st January 1950: British Steel Corporation, Tubes Division-Minerals from 29th March 1970.

This tramway was a direct replacement of the three-foot line already described and the main routes took largely the same courses toward the quarries. The line started from an end-on junction with the BR Denton branch, where accommodation for wagons was provided, and then curved to pass beneath the Denton-Harston road 300 yards west of the tree-lined narrow gauge cutting. On the north side was a weighbridge and brick cabin, and on the south side a single road shed of steel frame with corrugated iron and asbestos walls, suitable for three locomotives, and with a coal stage and water supply outside. In driving the tunnel under the road, some difficulty was experienced with repeated falls of earth, which delayed operations to the extent of causing the date incised on the south portal to be 1947, while that on the north was 1948. Beyond the locomotive shed the line divided, the westward branch roughly following the course of the former narrow gauge tramway, over the causeway and through the same tunnel beneath the Harston-Croxton Kerrial road, then over the Knipton-Croxton road by a gated level crossing, with a loop siding on the west side, to Cedar Hill quarries. Harston No. 2 quarry was served en route from a trailing junction west of the causeway (the narrow gauge had had a facing junction). The eastward branch by the locomotive shed crossed Green Lane on the level to enter Denton Park, and the line turned towards the road west of the narrow gauge course, as the workings were moving westwards. Except in the vicinity of the Denton branch, where bullhead rail was used, the track was flat-bottomed on wood or concrete sleepers and was very well laid.

The standard gauge line was brought into operation in July 1948, still serving 'Woolsthorpe Quarries' officially, a title hallowed by usage. The new system lacked the charm of the narrow gauge, with its variety of neat little engines and its happy unobtrusiveness on the rural scene, but the improvement in operating efficiency was obvious. No calcining was done, the ore being loaded directly into BR iron ore 'tipplers' at the working face. Over the period 1948-57 two locomotives were used, one working Denton Park and the other Harston No. 2. Cedar Hill quarries were not worked at this time and the line beyond the junction to Harston No. 2 was

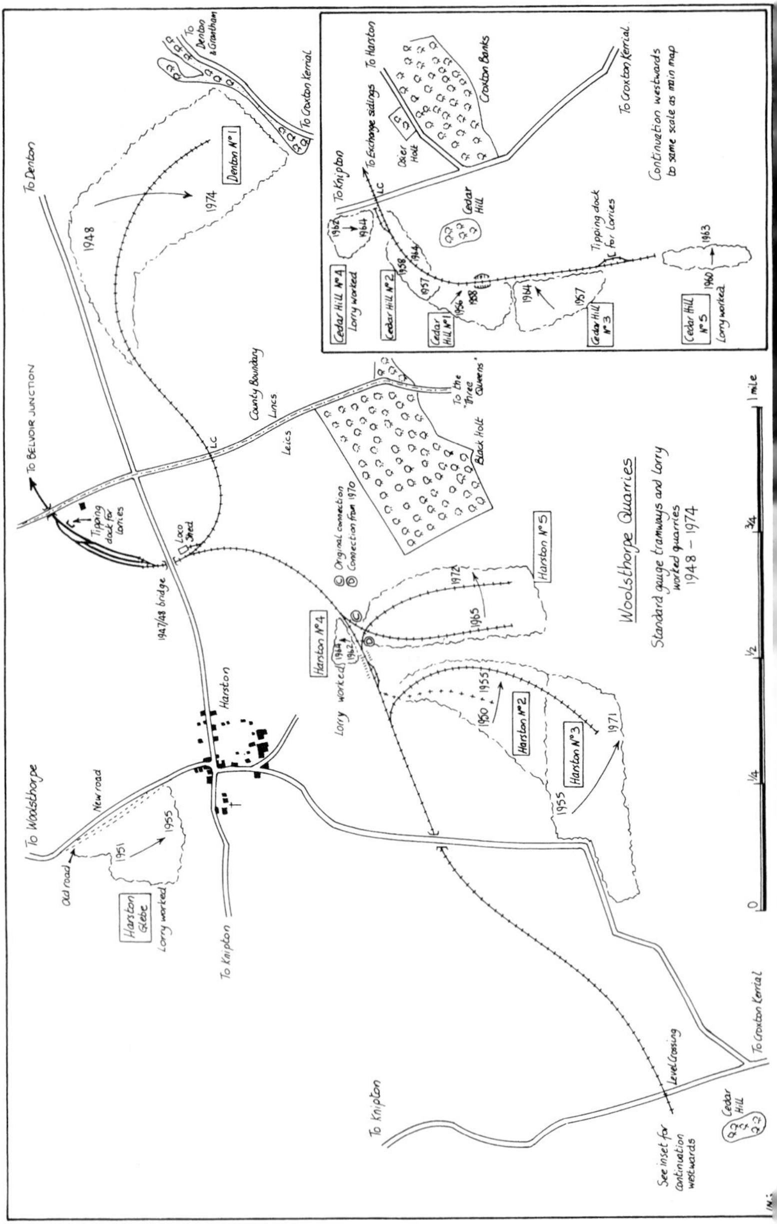
Woolsthorpe Quarries
Standard gauge tramways and lorry worked quarries
1948 – 1974
To Denton
To Denton & Grantham
To Croxton Kerrial
Denton No 1
1948
1974
To BELVOIR JUNCTION
Tipping dock for lorries
Loco Shed
1947/48 bridge
County Boundary
Lincs
Leics
LC
Black Holt
To the "Three Queens"
Original connection
Connection from 1970
Harston No 5
Harston No 4
Lorry worked
1965
1972
Harston No 2
Harston No 3
1950
1955
1971
Harston
To Woolsthorpe
New road
Old road
1951
Harston Glebe
Lorry worked
To Knipton
Level Crossing
Cedar Hill
See inset for continuation westwards
0
1/4
1/2
3/4
1 mile
To Harston
To Exchange sidings
Osier Holt
Croxton Banks
Cedar Hill No 4
Lorry worked
Cedar Hill No 2
Cedar Hill No 1
Cedar Hill No 3
Cedar Hill No 5
Tipping dock for Lorries
Continuation westwards to same scale as main map

therefore disused and its cinder ballast was overgrown; they were reopened in 1956 and two more locomotives were obtained to assist with the intensified working (actually three locomotives came, but HOLWELL No. 7 was only moved here as Eaton were dispensing with locomotive haulage). In the second half of 1958 the locomotive shed was extended to hold five engines.

The introduction of the standard gauge tramway permitted loading operations on a larger scale than the three-foot, and speeded up output as well; but the 'Harston' quarries – using this term to embrace all the quarries served by the tramway – were never very deep, so there was no need of the heavy machines used 'South of the Welland' at this time. A variety of draglines, mostly by Ruston Bucyrus, were acquired new or from other quarries, and their known duties are listed in the table. They were mostly of modest size, with one 100RB and, in the middle 1960s included two walking draglines, a W90 at Denton Park and a 5W at Harston No. 5 and then Denton Park.

Stewarts & Lloyds Minerals introduced where practicable the system of laying the rail tracks on the lip of the quarries instead of on the quarry floor. This had the twin advantages of a better surface for the track and elimination of the pull up from the quarry; but it could only be applied where the overburden was fairly shallow. The system was used at Cedar Hill, Harston No. 3 and Denton Park.

By the end of 1954 working at Harston No. 2 quarry had reached the edge of the outcrop on the west side of the small tributary of the Devon that the causeway crossed, and operations ceased here in 1955, as Harston No. 3 quarry was opened to the south, and served by an extension of the same branch tramway. The face of the quarry ran north-north-east to south-south-west, roughly parallel to the general trend of the Oolitic Cliff at this point, and working was in strips from north to south until increasing overburden put the work beyond the capabilities of the existing machines.

The next development was the Cedar Hill area, with a series of quarries strung along the narrowing valley west of Cedar Hill and about one mile east of Branston. The tramway ran generally north to south, with a loop near the level crossing and another at the southern end. Quarrying at Cedar Hill No. 1 was resumed in 1956 and went on for two years; also in 1956 was opened Cedar Hill No. 2, the small area between the standard gauge and former narrow gauge tramway routes east of the level crossing, and which was completed in about a year. Cedar Hill No. 3 was

Woolsthorpe Quarries. The south side of the bridge under the Harston road, with the standard gauge locomotive shed at right. When this photograph was taken on 18th December 1968 the shed had been extended forwards, as indicated by the different building type. This shed has now been re-erected at the Rutland Railway Museum. J. Bailey

Woolsthorpe Quarries. BELVOIR passes the locomotive shed with a loaded train from Denton Park. The extension to the shed is very clear, now with two 'pots'. August 1964. The 'green lane' lies behind the hedge in the background. P.H. Groom

Woolsthorpe Quarries. The roperunner completes his inspection of the empty wagons before SALMON takes the train to the quarries for loading on 8th August 1967. This view from the Harston road bridge shows the weigh house on the left, and in the background lies the tree-clad Oolitic escarpment. M.J. Leah.

Woolsthorpe Quarries. The Denton branch at Harston, looking towards Belvoir junction on 13th April 1972. On the right is the site of the tipping dock serving the Dairy Farm pits. J.R. Bonser

Woolsthorpe Quarries. Train on the Denton branch hauled by D8188 and D8122 on 13th April 1972. The Oolitic escarpment is clearly visible in the background. J.R. Bonser

Woolsthorpe Quarries. Denton Park quarry, showing how cultivation rapidly follows restoration of the ground. Machine is probably 43RB 6708. September 1953. BSC

opened in 1957, served from a trailing junction near the southern loop; this was the principal quarry and was worked until August 1964. These small faces of the Cedar Hill group were operated by machines of 37RB, 38RB, 43RB and 54RB types. Still further south was Cedar Hill No. 5, little more than a long strip along the rapidly narrowing valley; this was operated by lorries, for which a tipping dock was provided in 1960 at the rail loop. The stone was however relatively poor and the valley side soon made the overburden too heavy for the existing machines, and working was only from 1960 to August 1963. There was another lorry-worked pit, this time north of the level crossing; this was Cedar Hill No. 4, worked from 1962 to March 1964. Working of a narrow strip of ground south of the tramway made the official closure date of Cedar Hill No. 2 as January 1964, though in fact there had been no production here since 1958. Indeed, working at Cedar Hill generally was intermittent from 1962 onwards. Lifting of the Cedar Hill rail system began in 1964 and by June only some 200 yards of track were left beyond the level crossing, so presumably for the last workings the lorries had to take their loads to the Harston tip; further, the last loads from Cedar Hill No. 3 must have been removed by lorry. By the end of 1964 all track beyond the Croxton Kerrial road had been lifted but the level crossing gates were still in position. The enthusiast could obtain a useful birds eye view of the proceedings from the bridleway from Branston to Croxton.

While Cedar Hill was being closed, another quarry, Harston No. 5, was being opened up; this was on the opposite side of the valley to Harston No. 3, and was worked eastwards. A branch tramway was laid from a junction at the eastern end of the causeway and production commenced about January 1965. Trains for the Harston Nos 3/5 quarries usually consisted of ten wagons per trip, while at Denton Park only six were permitted because of the rather stiff climb out of the pit, that by then was close to the Melton Mowbray-Grantham road behind a belt of trees. Early in 1962 Denton Park quarry was temporarily closed and work was concentrated at Harston Nos 3 and 5 pits. Harston No. 4 quarry was a short-lived lorry-worked quarry, described below.

As the overburden increased in Harston No. 3, working by 43RB and 55RB machines was superseded by the 100RB (baring) and 55RB(loading), while at No. 5 the 5W walking dragline took over the baring from the 490 and 55RB. At Denton Park the 43RB did both baring and loading at first, later replaced by a 54RB. In the final stages the W90 performed the baring with loading by 490 and 55RB machines.

Woolsthorpe Quarries. Denton Park quarry, October 1962. The railway track stands on top of the orebed; in the foreground the ore has been blasted, and the next section is ready for drilling. 490 dragline stands ready for loading. BSC

Woolsthorpe Quarries. Cedar Hill No. 5 quarry in April 1960, with 37RB and 33RB machines driving the initial gullet. Cedar Hill stands at top centre. BSC

Woolsthorpe Quarries. Harston No. 5 quarry, October 1971. 5w walking dragline at quarry end; 490 shovel by railway wagons. BSC

The standard gauge system was almost entirely in the hands of Andrew Barclay six-coupled saddle tanks, and the class with 15-inch cylinders was adopted by Stanton as standard for quarry work. For the opening of the line SALMON (a 14-inch cylinder locomotive) was transferred from Harlaxton, plus a very small Hudsell Clarke 0-4-OST from Bowne & Shaw Ltd of Wirksworth, a Stanton subsidiary; a similar engine came in 1950 but these two were not big enough for the work (their cylinders had the same dimensions as the Hudswell Clarke 0-6-OST on the narrow gauge tramway) and they were scrapped when two new Barclays arrived. The latter were smartly kept in their livery of green lined black edged white, and perpetuated names associated with the narrow gauge, DENTON and BELVOIR, carried on brass plates contrary to Barclay's usual practice of applying names by transfers, as exemplified by SALMON. These three locomotives were later fitted with a type of water-softener made at Holwell works, sticking out at the front of the tank; and with neat grid-type spark arrestors to reduce the danger of damage to crops in fields bordering the line. Following the reopening of Cedar Hill quarries, three more locomotives were drafted to Harston; HOLWELL No. 7 from Eaton, another standard Barclay RUTLAND and the Hudswell Clarke SIR JOSEPH. The first came here because the rail system was being dispensed with at Eaton, and only did a couple of week's work before being sheeted over in the yard until she was cut up. SIR JOSEPH had a livery of green with red rods. SALMON went to Holwell works in June 1960 and was away for two years, returning in a livery of light green and red rods; the name was in plain red block lettering larger than the Andrew Barclay style, and later was altered to black letters with red shading; she also received a Stanton type chimney and 'pop' safety valves in place of spring-balance, and she faced the Denton branch instead of the other way round, as she had before. DENTON and RUTLAND also faced BR, white BELVOIR faced the quarry. By means of these and other trifling differences in cab windows, whistles, etc, it is possible to identify Barclays in photographs taken at Harston where the same is not recorded. The locomotives received plastic labels with plant numbers in the Stanton tradition,e.g. SALMON, DENTON, BELVOIR and RUTLAND were 8410/39, 8410/43, 8410/45, 8410/46 respectively.

In September 1958 a Ruston & Hornsby 0-4-ODH of class LSSH (No 437368) came on trials here and at Harlaxton, but the design was not adopted; she was probably satisfactory at Woolsthorpe but not powerful

Woolsthorpe Quarries. When the new standard gauge line was built, two Hudswell Clarke 0-4-0ST were brought in; but they were not up to heavy quarry work and were replaced by a series of Andrew Barclay 0-6-0STs. No 2 was photographed 25th July 1949.

K. Cooper/IRS collection

Woolsthorpe Quarries. Also at the opening was the AB 0-6-0ST SALMON, transferred from Harlaxton. Though similar in appearance to the later engines, she had only 14in cylinders, the others having 15in cylinders. She is now preserved by the RRM. 17th July 1949.

H. Gray

Woolsthorpe Quarries. One of the standard Andrew Barclay locomotives with 15ir cylinders, BELVOIR. Note water-softener on the smokebox front. The lettering of the nameplate is very similar to that on BELVOIR at Eastwell. S & L MINERALS LTD is paintec on the bunker, 21st September 1956. G. Alliez/courtesy B.D. Stoyel.

Woolsthorpe Quarries. The line to Cedar Hill passed beneath the Harston-Croxton Kerria road by a tunnel, widened when standard gauge was introduced. This view of the tunnel was taken on 23rd September 1971 after traffic had ceased. Compressor house at right.

Eric Tonks

enough for the more exacting conditions at Harlaxton.

The locomotive stock from 1962 onwards consisted of three Barclay 0-6-0ST of the four already mentioned, two normally being in steam. When demand slackened and Denton Park quarry was closed, DENTON was sent to Harlaxton (in April 1967) and the two remaining locomotives BELVOIR and SALMON were worked on alternate days, the two crews sharing the reduced work. In the middle of September 1967 came one of the Oxfordshire Ironstone diesels, MARY, in the smart livery of maroon lined black edged yellow and bearing a stencilled 'OXFORDSHIRE' on the step and a plant number 8411/04. MARY handled all the traffic from then onwards; the two remaining steamers were kept as spares but in fact they never hauled another wagonload of iron ore. Happily however both were saved by the preservation movement in places a long way from the ironstone country – SALMON to the North York Moors Railway (and later to the Rutland Railway Museum) and BELVOIR to the Stour Valley Railway at Chappel in Essex.

Wagons were normally 27-ton tipplers, which were preferred to hoppers, as they could be lifted wholesale. A feature of operation in later days was 'one way' working, where the locomotive pushed the empties to the quarry and hauled them back without running round; on the leading wagon was placed an electric 'bleeper' that emitted a penetrating whistle in the direction of travel, to warn quarrymen of the approach of the train. Track was mostly flat-bottomed, spiked to wooden sleepers, but later chaired track on concrete sleepers was favoured.

Harston No. 3 quarry was closed about Christmas time 1970, while at Harston No. 5 the facing junction was replaced by a reversing junction, as the working face by then demanded too sharp a curve on the former arrangement. The track beyond the Harston-Croxton road towards Cedar Hill had been lifted by early 1966, leaving a headshunt almost as far as the bridge; but with the closure of Harston No. 3 this section was lifted early in 1971, leaving just enough track over the causeway for a headshunt for No. 5 pit. Meanwhile, preparations to reopen Denton Park were under way, and when this was effected, Harston No. 5 was closed on 6th April, 1972. The line to the Harston quarries was lifted - including of course the section over the causeway – and the bridge under the Harston-Croxton road filled in, and even the corrugated iron parapets replaced by wire fencing; lifting was only dealt with slowly however, presumably by men not required for quarrying.

Demand at Scunthorpe, where all the output now went, fell as expected, and the operations had every appearance of a prelude to closure; by the autumn of 1973 quarrying was down to two days per week. The quarry itself was deeper than usual for this area, and the stiff climb and sharp curve out of the pit sometimes reduced the number of wagons to six or even four. Closure was then forecast for March 1974, which meant that parts of the Denton Park lease would not be required.

On the management side, Arthur Barber was in charge at first and on his retirement at the end of 1958 was replaced by Albert Bass, who later moved to Harlaxton when the two quarries were combined for administrative purposes. Other gentlemen associated with Woolsthorpe at this period were Mr. Crossland and Mr. Wakefield. But irrespective of who was in charge, the friendly cooperative atmosphere at Woolsthorpe (or Harston, as so many called it) was very obvious, a continuation of that esprit de corps built up in the days of the narrow gauge tramway; one sensed it was a happy place to work, and the welcome accorded visitors was legendary. Signatures in the Visitors Book consisted mainly of railway enthusiasts who had turned up without prior notice and were given permission to 'inspect the railway and take photographs'. More ambitious was the provision for parties to travel over the line in open wagons, with bales of hay provided as seats. The East Midlands Branch of the Railway Correspondence & Travel Society enjoyed on 6th July 1957 a tour behind BELVOIR as far as the level crossing on the Cedar Hill line, while a more elaborate tour on 30th September 1967 arranged for the Birmingham Locomotive Club and the Industrial Railway Society consisted of a run behind AJAX as far as the causeway, then back to the BR branch and over the latter to Harlaxton for a tour of that system. Memories of these events and of the numerous opportunities to see the quarries working in the ordinary way lent great poignancy to the closure in the eyes of railway enthusiasts, and to the workforce it meant a great deal more in the end of a way of life without parallel elsewhere. St. Valentine's Day 1974 was an easy date to remember and those who worked at Woolsthorpe are unlikely to forget it.

For several years Woolsthorpe and Harlaxton had been combined administratively and the closure of the two was integrated for Tuesday 14th February 1974. At Denton Park the last eight wagons were loaded by 11 o'clock and were taken away by MARY in two sets of four; by noon 91 years of quarrying at Woolsthorpe and of all Marlstone had come to an end. It is perhaps ironical that the publicity surrounding the closure of the Tubes Division Minerals last quarries North of the Welland was

Woolsthorpe Quarries. The last day of operations north of the Welland, 14th February 1974. MARY stands in Denton Park quarry while the wagons are loaded by the 55RB dragline. Albert Bass is by the locomotive, Eric Tonks watches the proceedings. J. Ginns

centred almost entirely on Harlaxton as the main producer but which historically only went back 33 years; Woolsthorpe was almost forgotten.

No time was lost in dismantling the remnants of the system. Of the line to the Harston quarries the rails had been lifted some time, but sleepers had been left in position; these were now taken up and by the end of April some were sold to the ill-fated scheme to relay the line from Market Overton to Saxby by Flying Scotsman Enterprises. At Denton Park track had been lifted back to the level crossing. The walking dragline was cut up at the end of 1973, the 490 in February 1974; the solitary locomotive MARY was moved to Harlaxton in February. By the summer all BSC track had been lifted as far as the BR Denton branch terminus, and a start had been made on restoring the quarry area to agriculture.

There were a number of offers from the railway preservation movement for the locomotive shed, which was purchased by the landowners, Welby Estates Ltd, as they were entitled to do under the terms of the lease. The first offer came from a Mr. B.W.M. Roberts of Tollerton, Nottinghamshire, who wished to bring here his locomotive, P1749, for which purpose he proposed leasing the shed and a length of track. This offer was turned down, and negotiations with the Keighley &

Worth Valley Railway did not come to anything. Eventually the building was purchased early in 1977 by Mr. F.G.Cann of Finedon and resold by him to the Market Overton Industrial Railway Association, who dismantled it and took the sections to Market Overton and then to Cottesmore when the Association moved there : it was erected in 1986.

Restoration proceeded steadily at the Harston quarries,and crops were growing on the site of the tramway late in 1974, but the quarry area took longer and was still being smoothed over twelve months later. A battery of earth-moving machines had been brought in and, once the general level was established, the men were left to work out for themselves the best way of achieving this, without undue supervision; this system appeared to work very well. Denton Park was still untouched, even the preliminary work having been hampered by the wet autumn of 1974; but by January 1976 restoration of Denton Park was complete, soon following on Harston Nos 3 and 5 quarries. The course of the line from the locomotive shed towards Green Lane was completely levelled and fenced off, though the level crossing notice was still to be found in the hedge. Even the tunnel under the Denton-Harston road was filled in with stone, though it had been stated that it would have lasted 'forever' and the brick and concrete parapets replaced by a wire and wood fence that certainly will not last so long. The narrow gauge locomotive shed and associated buildings on the north side were demolished in late January 1977.

Woolsthorpe Quarries. Green Lane, looking across the level crossing towards the trees of Black Holt on the escarpment. Note the low hedge on the extreme right, a replacement after the ground had been worked for ore; beyond it,the original hedge remains untouched.

Collection Eric Tonks

Woolsthorpe Quarries. The former narrow gauge locomotive shed 13th April 1972, externally hardly changed at all since last used. The hut to the left was finally used as an office by the surveyor, Bill Jones.
J.R. Bonser

Woolsthorpe Quarries. Company cottages at Harston. The tramway to the Dairy Farm pits ran across the ground in front of the cottages. To the left, the ground is rising to the tipping dock. 18th October 1988.
A.J. Cocklin

The extinction of these links left little of the once extensive Woolsthorpe quarries for the industrial archaeologist to find. We have already described the remains at Woolsthorpe proper (Brewer's Grave) but of the southern quarries grouped round Harston and Denton there was very little to be seen at all. The course of the BR Denton branch, lifted in the Spring of 1980, is still visible, and the cottages built by Stanton nearby are standing; the site of the tunnel where the narrow gauge passed under the Denton-Harston road is still marked by a wooden fence, and that of the standard gauge tunnel by a wire and wood fence. The sites of the buildings can be identified and the lorry tipping stage on the site of the rotary tippler is in position. The quarries for the most part were shallow, and even where the overburden was deeper on the south side the restoration had been so thorough as to leave few traces. Around Harston fields below road level tell their tale, but there are not many replacement hedges; even the altered course of the road from Harston towards Woolsthorpe is not at all readily apparent. If we leave Harston by Green Lane towards the main Grantham-Melton Mowbray road, we may note that the hedge on the east side is lower than that on the west, and consists solely of hawthorn and elder – and the level crossing site is marked by a hedge between wires; but as we climb the slopes and look down from the point where the bridleway enters the green glade of Black Holt, we cannot but reflect that the environmentalists can have no possible cause for complaint on the effects of nearly a century of ironstone quarrying. Most of us indeed would prefer to see the trains still moving along in their unobtrusive way.

The lorry-worked quarries

Lorry haulage at Woolsthorpe never attained the importance it had at Eaton and was always ancillary to, and not a substitute for, rail working. Three areas were dealt with – Harston Glebe, Harston No. 4 and some Cedar Hill quarries. The first was the largest and most important and was a continuation eastwards of some workings in the early 1900s south of Castle Farm on the west side of the road from Harston to Woolsthorpe; these workings and the mystery surrounding the transport method have been discussed earlier. East of the road the ground had been quarried 40 years before, and opportunity was taken to divert the road for the sake of the ore beneath its surface. The route was moved about a hundred feet east on to the exhausted ground for a distance of about one third of a mile from the bend immediately north of Harston village, to the next bend.

Woolsthorpe Quarries. Lorries were used at Harston to tackle some small areas. One of them was No. 4 quarry on the north side of the tramway. The machine is a 33RB dragline. 28th March 1962 BSC

Woolsthorpe Quarries. The lorry tipping dock on the site of the former narrow gauge tippler, at Harston sidings, 13th April 1972. Loaded wagons from the rail-worked quarries in the sidings. J.R. Bonser

Quarrying took place from 1951 to 1955, the lorries plying to and from a concrete tipping stage built on the site of the rotary tippler that had served the narrow gauge tramway. A small Ransomes & Rapier 431 diesel dragline was used at Harston Glebe.

Harston No. 4 quarry lay on the north side of the main Harston tramway, on the east side of the valley crossed by the causeway; its working life was short – opening in 1962 and closing in October 1964. The lorries travelled along the Harston-Denton road to the tipping stage as used by the lorries from Harston Glebe.

The third area served by lorry was Cedar Hill, and for this a special tipping dock was installed in 1960 on the loop line at the southern end of the Cedar Hill tramway. Two quarries were primarily involved – No. 5 at the southern tip of the valley, and No. 4 north of the level crossing with the Knipton-Croxton road. The dates of operation were 1960 to August 1963 for No. 5 quarry and 1962 to March 1964 for No. 4 quarry. Lorries were also used briefly to finish off operations at Cedar Hill Nos 2 and 3 quarries, but these workings as a whole were relatively small-scale. The tipping dock was dismantled in 1969.

Grid References

847349	Tipping dock, Bottesford Siding
846347	Top of incline
843346	Locomotive shed for Brewers Grave quarries
847337	Brewers Grave crossing
846334	'Dip' in Green Lane, north end
847327	'Dip' in Green Lane, south end
837327	South western extension to Castle Farm, terminus (approx.)
847323	Tipping stage on Denton Branch
847322	Main narrow gauge locomotive shed
848323	Cottages
849319	Level crossing, Green Lane
848321	Bridge under Denton Road
841312	Causeway over stream
838311	Bridge under Croxton Road
828303	Level crossing to Cedar Hill
845321	Locomotive shed on standard gauge extension, 1917
843322	Tipping stage to Std gauge Extension
850325	Locomotive shed, Dairy Farm pits
847320	Standard gauge Locomotive shed/Bridge under Denton Road
827290	Cedar Hill terminus
827291	Tipping dock for lorries, Cedar Hill
847323	Tipping dock for lorries to BR

Locomotives

Gauge: 3ft 0ins. Woolsthorpe Quarries (Brewer's Grave)

STANTON No. 9	0-4-2T	OC	JF	3866	c1880	7 x		(a)	(1)
STANTON No. 11	0-6-0ST	OC	HC	277	1885	9 x 15ins	2ft 6ins	New 4/1885	(2)
STANTON No. 12	0-6-0ST	OC	HC	429	1894	9½ x 15ins	2ft 6ins	(b)	(3)
STANTON No. 10	0-6-0ST	OC	HC	235	1882	9 x 15ins	2ft 6ins	(c)	(4)
NANCY	0-6-0T	OC	AE	1547	1908	10 x 16ins	2ft 6½ins	New 1908	(5)

(a) ex Wartnaby Quarries 11/1883
(b) ex Harston Quarries 1894
(c) ex Wartnaby Quarries c 1900
(1) to Harston Quarries c 1887
(2) to Harston Quarries c 1905
(3) to Wartnaby Quarries c 1900
(4) to Harston Quarries c 1908
(5) to Duke's Farm Quarries 1918

Gauge: 3ft 0ins. Duke's Farm Quarries, Woolsthorpe

NANCY	0-6-0T	OC	AE	1547	1908	10 x 16ins	2ft 6½ins	(a)	(1)

(a) ex Brewers Grave Quarries 1918
(1) to Harston Quarries 1923

Gauge: 3ft 0ins. Harston Quarries

STANTON No. 9	0-4-2T	OC	JF	3866	c1880	7 x		(a)	(1)
STANTON No. 12	0-6-0ST	OC	HC	429	1894	9½ x 15ins	2ft 6ins	New 11/1894	(2)
HARSTON (f. STANTON No. 14)	0-4-0ST	OC	WB	1587	1900	9 x 14ins	2ft 3½ins	New 2/1900	(3)
STANTON No. 11	0-6-0ST	OC	HC	277	1885	9 x 15ins	2ft 6ins	(b)	(4)
KNIPTON (f. STANTON No. 10)	0-6-0ST	OC	HC	235	1882	9 x 15ins	2ft 6ins	(c)	(5)
DENTON	0-4-0ST	OC	HC	506	1898	9 x 15ins	2ft 3ins	(d)	(6)
			Reb. Wake		1916				
STANTON No. 19	0-4-0ST	OC	MW	1038	1887	9½ x 14½ins	2ft 9ins	(e)	(7)
NANCY	0-6-0T	OC	AE	1547	1908	10 x 16ins	2ft 6½ins	(f)	(8)
WELBY (f. KITTY)	0-4-0ST	OC	HC	596	1901	9 x 15ins	2ft 6ins	(g)	(9)
			Reb. 1914						
BELVOIR	0-6-0ST	OC	HE	1823	1936	12 x 18ins	3ft 0ins	New 9/1936	(10)
HOLWELL No. 5	0-4-0ST	OC	P	1288	1912	10 x 15ins	2ft 6½ins	(h)	(9)

(a) ex Brewers Grave Quarries c 1887
(b) ex Brwers Grave Quarries c 1905
(c) ex Brewers Grave Quarries c 1908
(d) ex J. F. Wake, dealer, Darlington, 1916 (Orig. Newcastle & Gateshead Water Co.)
(e) ex Rothwell Hill Quarries c 1922
(f) ex Duke's Farm Quarries 1923

(g) ex HIW 1/1932 (prev. at Rothwell Hill Quarries)
(h) ex Eaton Quarries 4/1941

(1) to Stanton Ironworks for scrap 1912
(2) to Brewers Grave 1894; ex Eaton Quarries 1/1946; Scr by Thos W. Ward Ltd. 5/1950
(3) to Rothwell Hill Quarries c 1905
(4) to Tilton Quarries 2/1930
(5) to HIW 8/1923. then to Wartnaby Quarries. ex HIW 9/1928; to HIW 3/1937; ex HIW 6/1937. Scr by Thos W. Ward Ltd. 5/1950
(6) to HIW 2/1933; ex HIW 8/1933. To Tillton Quarries 7/1937
(7) to HIW, then to Nuthall Sandpits, Notts 10/1931
(8) to HIW 5/1936; ex HIW 8/1936; to HIW 9/1941; ex HIW 8/1942. To Eastwell Iron Ore Co Ltd. 8/1950
(9) Scr by Thos W. Ward Ltd. 5/1950
(10) to HIW 11/1942; ex HIW 2/1943. To Eastwell Iron Ore Co Ltd 8/1950

Gauge: 4ft 8½ins. Harston Quarries north of main line

STANTON No. 8	0-4-0ST	OC	N	1941	1874	12 x 20ins	(a)	(1)
HOLWELL No. 9 (?)	0-6-0ST	IC	HC				(b)	(2)

(a) ex Stanton Ironworks c 1917
(b) ex Buckminster Quarries c 1924

(1) to Eaton Quarries c 1924
(2) to Buckminster Quarries 1925

Gauge: 4ft 8½ins. Harston Quarries south of the main line.

	4w PMR			R&R	1934	24hp		(a)	s/s
No. 2		0-4-0ST	OC	HC 1605	1927	9 x 15ins	2ft 6½ins	(b)	Scr 1952
	SALMON	0-6-0ST	OC	AB 2139	1942	14 x 22ins	3ft 5ins	(c)	(1)
No. 1		0-4-0ST	OC	HC 1215	1917	9 x 15ins	2ft 6ins	(d)	Scr 9/1953
	DENTON	0-6-0ST	OC	AB 2306	1951	15 x 22ins	3ft 5ins	New 7/1951	(2)
	AJAX	0-6-0T	OC	AB 1605	1918	16 x 24ins	3ft 7ins	(e)	(3)
	BELVOIR	0-6-0ST	OC	AB 2350	1954	15 x 22ins	3ft 5ins	New 1/1954	(4)
	HOLWELL No. 7	0-6-0ST	IC	MW 556 Reb. Holwell 1949	1875	12 x 17ins	3ft 0ins	(f)	(5)
	RUTLAND	0-6-0ST	OC	AB 2351	1954	15 x 22ins	3ft 5ins	(g)	(6)
No. 236	SIR JOSEPH	0-6-0ST	OC	HC 1196	1916	14 x 20ins	3ft 7ins	(h)	(7)
	MARY	0-4-0DH		RR 10203	1964	311hp	30 tons	(i)	(8)

(a) ex Buckminster Quarries c 1947
(b) ex Bowne & Shaw Ltd, Wirksworth, Derbyshire 4/1948
(c) ex Harlaxton Quarries 5/1948
(d) ex Bowne & Shaw Ltd 1/1950
(e) ex Buckminster Quarries 1/1952
(f) ex Eaton Quarries 10/1957
(g) ex Market Overton Quarries 5/1958
(h) ex Harlaxton Quarries 11/1958

(i) ex Oxfordshire Ironstone Co Ltd 9/1967

(1) to North York Moors Railway 3/1969
(2) to Harlaxton Quarries 10/1962; ex Harlaxton 3/1964; to Harlaxton 4/1967
(3) to Buckminster Quarries 5/1952
(4) to Stour Valley Railway Preservation Society, Chappel, Essex, 1/1972
(5) Scr on site by John Lee & Son (Grantham) Ltd 9/1960
(6) to Harlaxton Quarries 1/1964
(7) to Harlaxton Quarries 1/1960
(8) to Harlaxton Quarries 3/1974

Quarry Machines

No. 20	S. Shovel	RP	488	1917	2½Cu. Yds.	26ft.	New 8/1917 (a)	(1)
No. 10	S. Dragline	RH	981	1925	¾Cu. Yd.	50ft.	New 2/1925 (b)	(2)
No. 10	S. Dragline. Caterpillar	RH	1178	1928	1½Cu. Yds.	45ft.	(c)	(3)
43RB	D. Shovel. Caterpillar	RB	4763	1939	1½Cu. Yds.	50ft.	(d)	(4)
37RB	D. Dragline	RB	3344	1937	1½Cu. Yds.	40ft.	(e)	(5)
21RB	D. Dragline	RB	3306	1937	⅜Cu. Yd.	50ft.	(f)	(6)
No. 4	S. Shovel	RH	1119	1927	1½Cu. Yds.	30ft 6ins.	(g)	(7)
55RB	E. Crane. Crawler	RB	4975	1940	2 Cu. Yds.	60ft.	(h)	(8)
43RB	D. Dragline. Crawler	RB	6708	1941	1 Cu. Yd.	75ft.	(i)	(9)
422	D. Dragline	R&R	619	1937	½Cu. Yd.	35ft.	(j)	(10)
43RB	D. Shovel	RB	11318	1948	1½Cu. Yds.	50ft.	New 6/1948	(11)
431	D. Dragline	R&R	451	1936	½Cu. Yd.	50ft.	(k)	(12)
55RB	E. Dragline/Crane	RB	5706	1941	1½Cu. Yds.	60ft.	(l)	(13)
43RB	D. Dragline	RB	3015	1936	1½Cu. Yds.	40ft.	(m)	(14)
33RB	D. Dragline	RB	21249	1956	1¼Cu. Yds.		New 5/1956	(15)
54RB	D. Dragline	RB	21889	1957	2¾Cu. Yds.	60ft.	New 5/1957	(16)
54RB	D. Dragline	RB	22364	1957	2¾Cu. Yds.	60ft.	New 7/1957	(17)
38RB	D. Dragline	RB	21896	1957	1 Cu. Yd.	60ft.	New 10/1957	(18)
43RB	D. Shovel	RB	5664	1941			(n)	(19)
100RB No. 215	E. Dragline. Caterpillar	RB	3682	1938	4 Cu. Yds.	60ft.	(o)	(20)
490	E. Dragline	R&R	1192	1941	2 Cu. Yds.	75ft.	(p)	(21)
W90	E. Walking Dragline	R&R	1693	1945	1½Cu. yds.	127ft.	(q)	(22)
10RB	D. Dragline	RB	18290	1954	10 Cu. Ft.	35ft.	(r)	(23)
5W	E. Walking Dragline	RB	21407	1956	4 Cu. Yds.	135ft.	(s)	(24)
54RB	D. Shovel	RB	22150	1957			(t)	(25)

(a) Converted to Dragline 9/1926 – 1¾Cu. Yds. 54ft.
(b) Later with 1 Cu. Yd. bucket.
(c) ex Vale's Plant Register 3/1937
(d) ex Glendon Quarries 5/1940. Later with 1¼Cu. yds. 60ft.
(e) ex Royal Navy Fuel Depot, Torpoint, per Abelson & Co (Engineers) Ltd, Sheldon, Birmingham 5/1940. Converted to Shovel 1957 – 1¼Cu. yds. 23ft.
(f) ex Eaton Quarries 8/1940
(g) ex London Brick Co Ltd, Peterborough, 3/1942, per C. Jones Ltd, dealer, Aldridge, Staffordshire. Front end fitted at Woolsthorpe.
(h) ex Harlaxton Quarries 10/1945. later with 1¾Cu. Yds. 22ft.
(i) ex Brymbo Steel Co Ltd, Hook Norton quarries, Oxfordshire, per MOS 10/1946

(j) ex Eaton Quarries 6/1947
(k) ex Tilton Quarries 6/1951
(l) ex Harlaxton Quarries 12/1952. Later (1955) with 2½ Cu. Yds. 60ft.
(m) ex Market Overton Quarries 1954
(n) ex Harlaxton Quarries 1957
(o) ex Market Overton Quarries 10/1958
(p) ex Harlaxton Quarries in the 1960s.
(q) ex Holwell Quarries c 1962. Later with 2 Cu. Yds, 113ft. 6ins.
(r) ex Eaton Quarries c 1962
(s) ex Pitsford Quarries, Northamptonshire late 1965
(t) ex Harlaxton Quarries c 1967

(1) At Harston North quarry; at Harston South qy. 1925. Wrecked 12/1941 (per Stanton records)
(2) At Dairy Farm qy.; to Knipton qy. 1931; to Beasleys qy.; To Holwell Works 11/1947
(3) At Knipton qy.(?). Scr 1/1952
(4) To Holwell Quarries 1/1943
(5) At Harston Glebe qy.; to Cedar Hill qys. 11/1955. Scr
(6) To Glendon Quarries 10/1940
(7) At Knipton qy.; to Denton Park qy. Scr 11/1945
(8) At Harston No. 2 qy.; to Bowne & Shaw Ltd, Wirksworth, Derbyshire 6/1946; ex Bowne & Shaw; at Harston No. 2 qy. to Eaton Quarries 11/1949. Ex Wirksworth Quarries 5/1955. To Market Overton Quarries 12/1955
(9) At Denton Park qy. To Stanton Ironworks 7/1957
(10) Ancillary machine. To South Witham Quarries 11/1948
(11) New to Denton Park qy. To Harlaxton Quarries
(12) At Harston Glebe qy. To Market Overton Quarries c 2/1955
(13) At Harston No. 3 qy.; to Harston No. 5 qy.; to Harston No. 3 qy. to Denton Park qy., 3/1971. Scr. 1974
(14) Probably at Harston No. 2 qy.; to Harston No. 3 qy. To Harlaxton Quarries 3/1956
(15) New to Harston No. 3 qy.; to Harston No. 4 qy. To Buckminster Quarries
(16) New to Denton Park qy.; to Cedar Hill No. 5 qy. To Harlaxton Quarries.
(17) New to Denton Park qy. To Buckminster Quarries 8/1957 (some confustion exists concerning these two 54RB machines and intermediate moves might be ascribable to the other machine)
(18) New to Cedar Hill qys. To Corby Quarries 10/1963
(19) At Cedar Hill qys. To Stanton Ironworks 1/1962
(20) At Harston No. 3 qy. To Market Overton Quarries.
(21) At Harston No. 3 qy.; to Harston No. 5 qy. 3/1971. To Denton Park qy. Scr 2/1974
(22) At Denton Park qy. Scr 11-12/ 1973
(23) Ancillary machine. To Stanton Estates Dept 9/1964
(24) At Harston No. 5 qy. To Denton Park qy., Scr 1972-3
(25) At Harston No. 3 qy. To Denton Park qy. (?). To Harlaxton Quarries.

THE OUTLYING QUARRIES

The three quarry systems described in this section are all isolated from others in the county, and we place them together simply on that basis.

Sproxton quarries bear close relationships, in geology, history and operating methods, to the United Steel's Colsterworth quarries of Lincolnshire, and in its later years was associated with them by management. Like them, it was served by the LNER High Dyke mineral branch, which at Sproxton seemed to finish almost in mid-air; the section from Skillington Road Junction was in fact the only portion constructed of a proposed cross-country line linking up at Waltham-on-the-Wolds with the Eaton branch. Sproxton was a purely 20th century system and in its later stages the quarries were worked entirely by lorries.Quarrying at Tilton only came about because of the building of the GNR-LNWR Joint line, which exposed a layer of ironstone in Tilton cutting. But what a gem it was! Because of its isolation it was not much visited by enthusiasts, but there is no doubt it was one of the most picturesque of Midlands ironstone quarries. There were several changes in the manner in which the ore was brought down from the quarries to the main line, all of considerable interest.

Whilst Tilton was in the Marlstone Rock, the isolated outcrop of Nevill Holt was in the Northampton Sand. The involved history of this site – greater than the meagre output warranted – is of interest if only to demonstrate the folly of over-optimism. The remains on site are interesting, and the setting very pleasant indeed.

SPROXTON QUARRIES

Owners: Park Gate Iron & Steel Co Ltd: British Steel Corporation, Northern & Tubes Group from 1st July 1968; British Steel Corporation, Scunthorpe Division, Ore Mining Branch from 1st September 1969.

The Great Northern Railway High Dyke branch was built to convey iron ore to Scunthorpe, first from Buckminster (Stainby) quarries, and, soon after, from the newly opened Colsterworth quarries; Sproxton quarries could be described as a secondary development, for while they would hardly have been considered but for the proximity of High Dyke, a branch line from the latter was required to give rail access. The precise date of opening of the branch from Skillington Junction has not so far turned up, but amongst the Belvoir Estate papers is a lease dated 3rd December 1921 for ground for 'the proposed Great Northern Railway branch to Sproxton', which suggests the line was built shortly afterwards. The terminus was sited by the Sproxton-Saltby road, with a number of sidings well above the level of the road, which dips at this point. Sproxton is just inside Leicestershire.

The quarrying area was leased from the Belvoir Estate and work on opening up started in 1921, but ironstone was not despatched until April 1925, possibly because of the postwar drop in demand, and for some years was only on a small scale. The quarry lay between the GNR terminus and Sproxton village, and was worked from west to east, with in early days an extraordinary variety of transport methods. The Day Books preserved in Leicestershire Record Office contain records of payments in the period July 1925 to March 1928 to Staveley Coal & Iron Co Ltd (variously at Pilton, Eastwell and Pitsford) for the hire of track and Jubilee wagons; this narrow gauge system was probably for carrying away soil or overburden. No locomotive is mentioned. The standard gauge quarry tramway was a very simple one, consisting merely of a line from the LNER as far as the Sproxton-Saltby road, with a reversing line to the quarry and one siding for wagons. According to Mr Coy (later manager at Eastwell) for the first two or three years horses were used to haul wagons up from the pit, but they found it such hard going that stationary traction engine haulage was used for two more years or so. Horse haulage on standard gauge quarry lines was a rarity at any time, and for it to be used on a brand-new line, however short, in the post-World War I period is remarkable. The Day Books record the 'hire of an engine' from Beeby

Sproxton Quarries. For the first two or three years the wagons were pulled by horses, an unusual arrangement for a standard gauge line, and our picture shows two hopper wagons in the charge of two horses, about 1926. The going was so hard that a stationary traction engine was introduced, and then locomotives from 1931. RRM Archives

Sproxton Quarries. A 1930s view of No. 1 quarry with transporter, No. 20 shovel and No. 15 shovel. Note in the foreground the very high trestles across the gullet; it would take nerve to push barrows across this spidery bridge! RRM Archives

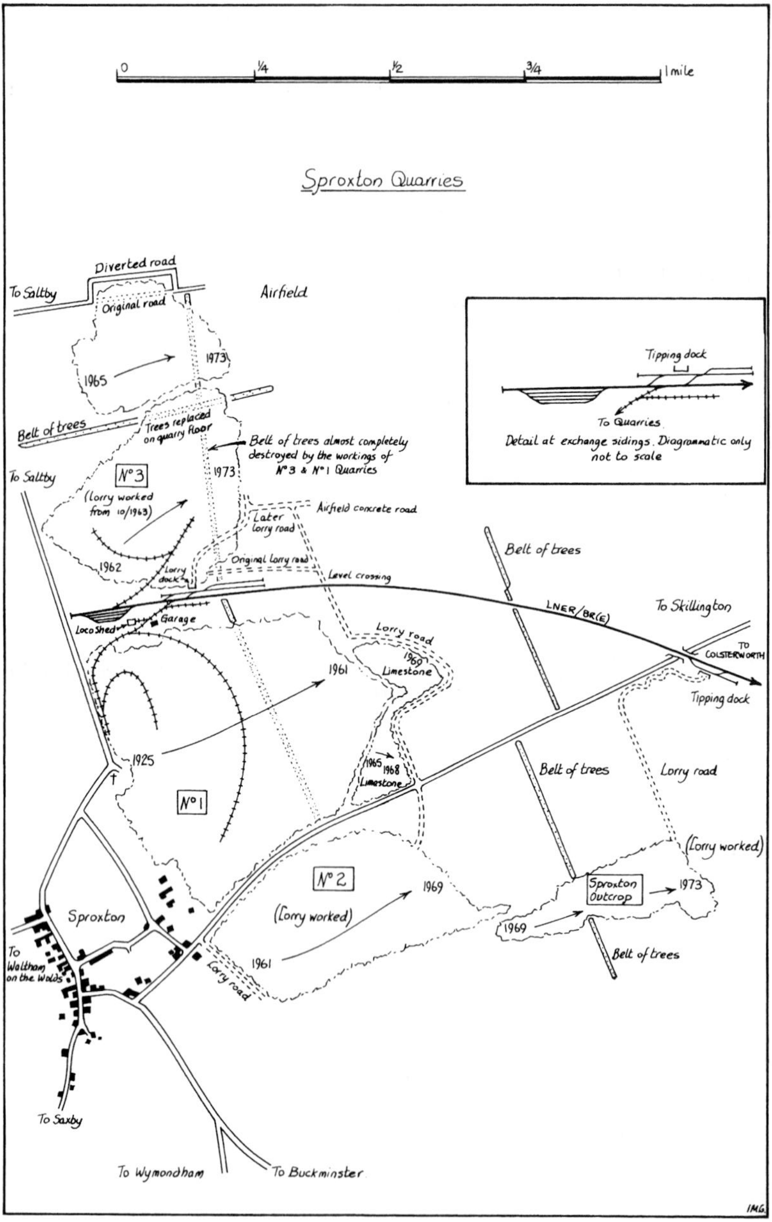
0
1/4
1/2
3/4
1 mile
Sproxton Quarries
Diverted road
To Saltby
Original road
Airfield
1965
1973
Belt of trees
Trees replaced on quarry floor
Belt of trees almost completely destroyed by the workings of N° 3 & N° 1 Quarries
To Saltby
N° 3
(Lorry worked from 10/1963)
1973
Airfield concrete road
Later lorry road
1962
Original lorry road
Lorry dock
Level crossing
Belt of trees
LNER/BR(E)
To Skillington
Loco Shed
Garage
Lorry road
1969 Limestone
1961
TO COLSTERWORTH
Tipping dock
1925
1965 1968 Limestone
Belt of trees
Lorry road
N° 1
N° 2
(Lorry worked)
Sproxton
1969
(Lorry worked)
1961
Sproxton Outcrop
1973
1969
Belt of trees
To Waltham on the Wolds
Lorry road
To Saxby
To Wymondham
To Buckminster
Tipping dock
To Quarries
Detail at exchange sidings. Diagrammatic only not to scale
IMG

Bros March 1928 to March 1932, tying in with information obtained from Beeby in 1950 by Eric Hannan, of a John Fowler single-cylinder petrol-electric machine (registration AL 8346) "sold to Park Gate, Sproxton, for top soil removal and ore loading to wagons". In November 1931 however a locomotive appeared on the scene in the form of an ancient Manning Wardle outcast from Park Gate ironworks, and which had seen earlier service at Scunthorpe quarries. An elderly employee at Park Gate told Ken Plant that he remembered her going to Sproxton; he also remembered her return in the form of a wagon load of scrap containing several identifiable items such as the chimney and saddle tank! In 1935 a Hunslet replacement was sent; this machine, HASTINGS, though only junior to No.5 by a few years, seems to have been well liked, her six wheels no doubt giving her a considerable advantage over the four-wheeler. As the working face moved eastward, the line to the Saltby road was abandoned and replaced by a new direct line into the pit at a very steep gradient. A third locomotive arrived during World War II, another Manning Wardle but this time a comparatively modern one that had been supplied new to Charwelton quarries and made redundant there by the arrival of more powerful new locomotives. It is likely that both locomotives worked during the remaining war years, but afterwards CHARWELTON (familiarly known as 'Charlie') did most of the work, with HASTINGS spare. Both were kept in nice clean condition and were in a livery of chocolate brown with black and yellow lining, that in the case of CHARWELTON had the ornateness characteristic of a showman's engine.

A locomotive shed was built at an unknown date, but presumably when HASTINGS arrived; it was unusual in being very much in the early 'Army Hut' style, of creosoted slatted wood and with window frames painted white. The office was incorporated in the same building and it is possible that the locomotive shed was merely an extension of this; certainly it looked very unlike a locomotive shed, most of which tend to be higher than they are wide. Eaton Ropeway had a wooden shed, but this was of traditional dimensions; Sproxton looked like an army or contractor's hut, only the 'pots' giving away its true purpose. Even these were unusual, the smoke vents inside the shed being fitted with a wonderful contraption by which they could be lowered over the locomotive chimneys; a refinement introduced undoubtedly because of the low wooden roof. The shed was further extended in late 1957 to accommodate another locomotive obtained in anticipation of increased output. She was one of four

Sproxton Quarries. No photograph of the first locomotive seems to have survived but the others have all been recorded. The one shown is HASTINGS, vintage Hunslet of 1888, shown here on 23rd March 1954 on the line to the quarry. Note the 'army hut' locomotive shed and water tower. J.R. Bonser

Sproxton Quarries. HASTING's shed-mate for 40 years was CHARWELTON, from the quarries near Banbury. She is shown here at work in No. 3 quarry on 18th April 1963; six weeks later, lorries took over the work. The loading machine is a 490 high-lift shovel. R.K. Hateley

Sproxton Quarries. The last locomotive was a Hudswell Clarke displaced from Appleby-Frodingham steelworks, and came in 1951. She is here shown on 17th May 1962 marshalling wagons for the BR sidings.
Ivo Peters

purchased by Staveley Iron & Chemical Co Ltd from Appleby-Frodingham steelworks for quarry work, and in the Sproxton shed was repaired and repainted in the Staveley livery of light green with red rods. Not long before this, the three quarries in the Midlands owned by Park Gate (Sproxton; Eaton Basic; Charwelton) were placed under the control of the area managers of Staveley Iron & Chemical Co Ltd. Sproxton and Eaton were managed along with Eastwell, Waltham etc. One effect of this was the transfer of fitters here from Waltham in 1958.

At the beginning of 1959 the quarry – No. 1 quarry, no other having been started – was coming to the end of its useful life. Working had moved from the Croxton Kerrial road eastwards, and the layout had been modified, e.g. the point of connection of the quarry line with the line on the top running towards BR. The gradient was against the load, and the quarry so deep that CHARWELTON could manage only two 27-ton wagons per trip. HASTINGS had been out of use for some time (the last spares for her came at the end of 1956), as being too light for the work, and having no steam brake; on one occasion the load was too much and she ran back into the pit, severing the power supply to the excavator but nothing worse. Through most of 1960 the Hudswell Clarke was the working engine, but CHARWELTON was back in harness at the end of the year and seems to have carried on until the quarry closed about July 1961. By then working had extended greatly eastwards, breaching the half-mile belt of trees between railway and the Skillington road; increasing cover brought ironstone quarrying to an end, but working of overlying limestone continued further east up to 1969.

South of the Skillington road, immediately east of the village, land owned by the Buckminster Trust Estate was part of the former Stanton lease, but on 31st July 1954 Park Gate had obtained the lessor's consent to work the area, which they now took up as No 2 quarry. Work on the 'Skillington Road Development' gets frequent mention in the Day Books for 1960/1 and production seems to have commenced about April 1961, when two Euclid 27-ton dumptrucks were hired, while in December 1961 some AEC dumptrucks were hired from Desborough quarries. Lorry haulage of ironstone was to achieve its greatest development at Sproxton, starting with No. 2 quarry. A lorry road was laid alongside the western edge of the opening gullet to the Skillington road, along which the loaded vehicles travelled half a mile, then took to another private road that skirted No.1 quarry, used an accommodation crossing to reach the north side of the BR line, then paralleled the latter to a concrete tipping

Sproxton Quarries. View along the High Dyke line, looking across the level crossing towards Sproxton, 15th September 1963. The trailing siding later served the tipping dock where lorries from the Outcrop quarry left their loads. Note one of the belts of trees planted as windbreaks in this bleak area. G. Ordish

Sproxton Quarries. A class O1 locomotive hauling a train of empties, approaching Skillington crossing, 9th August 1963. G. Ordish

Sproxton Quarries. No. 3 quarry, with the top 15 feet of Lincolnshire Limestone being removed by a 43RB dragline and loaded into lorries. 27th April 1960 D.H. Newman

Sproxton Quarries. 5360 stripping shovel being moved across the road into No. 3 quarry in March 1962. D.H. Newman

dock at the junction of two new storage sidings. From these wagons were allowed to run by gravity and, after loading, were collected in the sidings at the end of the BR branch.

Rail haulage was not finished, however, and was used at another new quarry, No. 3 (or West) quarry, north of the BR branch, the connection making a trailing link (viewed from Colsterworth) with the northernmost siding; otherwise the layout was almost a mirror image of the old one to the south. In February 1962 the 5360 shovel was moved over from No.1 quarry; this was done overland, as being cheaper than dismantling and re-erecting, the road being closed for the day. Production at No. 3 started in the same month, with CHARWELTON struggling as before to haul two loaded wagons from the pit; she returned to the shed via the BR line after the day's work. In the summer of 1963 it was announced that haulage by Scammell lorries would supersede rail at No. 3 quarry, the date quoted being 1st September 1963, but in fact the changeover did not take place until 18th October. Access to the tipping dock was short and direct, but the advancing face of No. 3 quarry caused a deviation of the lorry road from No. 2; after crossing the railway, the road ran north-north-west for about 300 yards, then turned west, utilizing a section of concrete road that was formerly part of the disused Saltby airfield system, and then descended the face of No. 3 quarry by a prepared slope to reach the dock. The overland route south of the railway was diverted eastwards around the new limestone workings at No. 1, and crossed the Skillington road to drop steeply down to the face on the east side.

With lorries firmly in control in all working quarries, no time was lost in disposing of the redundant locomotives; HASTINGS had been relegated to the end of the sidings alongside the BR branch early in 1960, but she was moved to a siding near the office in October 1963. She and CHARWELTON departed for preservation by the revived Kent & East Sussex Railway on New Year's Eve, leaving the Hudswell Clarke in solitary state in the locomotive shed until she was moved to quarries at Scunthorpe. Two of the smoke chutes were dismantled and put to further service at Byfield locomotive shed, where they were recognised by Roger West in February 1965. The lorries continued to rumble along the special roads, performing their job efficiently but hardly picturesquely, and in 1968 the Scammells were replaced by a fleet of six Euclid 35-ton dumptrucks.

One more quarry remains to be described; for some reason this was not called No. 4 but simply 'Sproxton Outcrop'; it lay due east of No. 2

quarry, and about half a mile across the valley from Buckminster's No. 15 quarry. As implied by the name, the ground falls away here and the stone was under shallower cover; it was worked in strips from west to east along the outcrop. Production commenced in 1968, with lorries taking the output to a separate tipping dock on the south side of the BR line east of the level crossing with the Skillington road, where the railway accommodation was of the simplest – a single siding making a trailing junction with the High Dyke line, so that trains of empties had to 'set back' for loading; but, later, facing points were installed to ease matters. The lorry road between dock and quarry ran parallel to the public road for about 400 yards before turning south-south-east by a barn. These lorry roads were mostly of packed limestone rubble.

Having described at length the complicated transport arrangements at Sproxton, it is time we had a look at the quarry machines. A Ruston & Hornsby 20-ton steam 'combined excavator and grab' came in 1924 and probably sufficed up to the 1930 period, when another steam shovel and transporter were acquired secondhand. In 1940 a Ransomes & Rapier 5360 electric shovel was installed and was responsible for shifting most of the overburden thenceforward in Nos 1 and 3 quarries. In 1948 Ransomes & Rapier also supplied two 490 electric machines, a dragline and a shovel, the latter presumably for loading, and the other helping as required. No more machines came new, but a wide variety came secondhand, including some from other Park Gate quarries, and from Eastwell and Waltham; amongst the latter a 24RB (No. 4951) had already been hired from Waltham during the war. These machines were mostly smaller diesel types, used on miscellaneous tasks associated with opening up new faces and on restoration work, etc; but a 5W diesel-electric walking dragline came from Holwell in1960 and worked in No. 2 quarry along with a 54RB for loading; the 5W later worked the Outcrop quarry, and probably the 54RB did also. A 480 shovel came from Cringle in October 1960 to work No. 1 quarry. In 1961 a Ransomes & Rapier S 1500 machine was quoted for (per correspondence kindly shown us by Bert Smith of Cranford) but this was not implemented.

Upon nationalization (1st July 1968) Sproxton was placed in the Northern & Tubes Group of the British Steel Corporation along with other quarries in the Staveley group of Stewarts & Lloyds Minerals; but it was soon realised that Sproxton had more affinities with the United Steels group, and from 1st September 1969 was transferred to the Ore Mining Branch of the Scunthorpe Division. This was logical not only geographically but mechanically. Sproxton had gone over completely to lorry operation and, as we have seen, United Steels planned to do the same thing at Colsterworth and, had these plans come to fruition, it would have been possible to develop further areas near Saltby by a branch off United Steel's roadway. As at Colsterworth, work ceased at Sproxton on 3rd April 1973, the end hastened by a few weeks by a strike at Scunthorpe; and it is believed that there was no resumption. The last lorry load came from No. 3 quarry.

The remains at Sproxton are reasonably extensive; not much of the tramway system is visible, of course, as in the quarry areas it was engulfed by lorry operations; but there are traces in the former yard, including the wooden locomotive shed with its one pot – though, shorn of its smoke vents, it looks more like an army hut than ever! A section with lower windows is the extension. Nearby is the tall lorry shed of green corrugated iron, and a petrol pump stands between the two. The dilapidated mess hut of corrugated iron, with wooden benches, bears witness to the rough conditions of the quarrymen's life, and there was still in 1989 a notice 'Beware of Trains'. The north terminal face of No. 3 quarry has been smoothed over but is still recognisable for what it was – and the narrow lane along the edge still has the kink in it made to allow a few more yards of working. The eastern slope has a cliff-like face except where built up for the rough lorry road out of it. Extension of the quarry had led to the destruction of one of the belts of trees so characteristic of this windswept part of the country, and this has been replaced on the same site but at the much lower contour. This was presumably in accordance with the terms of the lease, but if the purpose of the trees was to provide a windbreak, it hardly fulfils that purpose now! On the restored land, wire fences are much in evidence, and the lorry road is still traceable, including the concrete section formerly part of Saltby Airfield.

An afforested slope marks the termination of the northern part of No. 1 quarry, and at one point an artificial bank has been built across the hollow, with a hedge between wires along the top. This is well beyond the long belt of trees destroyed in the later excavations. The deep terminal gullet, water-filled, stretches nearly to the Skillington road. The limestone quarry to the east presents a very different and distinctly curious appearance, with a carpet of deep green grass upon which cattle graze. The older part of No. 1 quarry near the village has been fully restored, but retains the slight depressions and hummocky appearance often associated with early restoration.

Sproxton Quarries. The black flag denotes that this was the last load of iron ore on the Hig
Dyke branch from Sproxton quarries, crossing Skillington Road on 3rd April 1973.
RRM Archive

Sproxton Quarries. The former locomotive shed on 17th March 1979, with the BR trackbe
to the right. The building never looked much like a loco.shed even when in use! Eric Tonk

At No. 2 quarry the west end near Sproxton village has been restored to agriculture, the rest afforested except for the final gullet; the course of the lorry road is clear. Sproxton Outcrop pit is less well-defined because it was shallower and easier to restore, but if one follows the lorry route, the normal hedge gives way to a new hawthorn hedge between wires, with the quarry area to the west. The site of the tipping dock by the BR line can also be seen.

Grid References

858254	Junction with GNR branch
857254	Locomotive shed
863251	No. 1 quarry terminus (gullet)
857254	No. 2 quarry terminus (face)
866219	No. 1A quarry - level crossing for lorries
875245	No. 3 quarry entrance
862255	Tipping dock for Nos 1 and 2 quarries
875253	Tipping dock for No. 3 quarry
864253	Level crossing - lorry road/railway
867252	Limestone quarry, east end
873248	Outcrop quarry - north east corner
873253	Tipping dock for Outcrop quarry

Locomotives

Gauge: 4ft 8½ins

PARKGATE No. 5	0-4-0ST	OC	MW	700	1879	12 x 18ins	3ft 0ins	(a)	Scr 1937
HASTINGS	0-6-0ST	IC	HE	469	1888	13 x 18ins	3ft 1ins	(b)	(1)
CHARWELTON	0-6-0ST	IC	MW	1955	1917	15 x 22ins	3ft 9ins	(c)	(1)
–	0-6-0ST	OC	HC	1630	1929	15 x 22ins	3ft 4ins	(d)	(2)

(a) ex Park Gate Ironworks, Rotherham, 11/1931
(b) ex Park Gate Ironworks, 6/1935
(c) ex Charwelton Quarries, near Banbury, c 3/1942
(d) ex Appleby-Frodingham Steel Co, Scunthorpe. 10/1957
(1) to Kent & East Sussex Railway Preservation Society, 31/12/1963
(2) to Byfield Ironstone Co Ltd, Midland Quarries, Scunthorpe, c 4/1964

Quarry Machines

No. 20	S. Combined Shovel and Grab	RH	649	1920	2¾Cu. Yds.	26ft.	(a)	(1)
No. 5	SND Transporter	RH	530	1919			(b)	(2)
No. 15	S. Shovel	RH	705	1922	2¼Cu. Yds.	28ft.	(c)	(3)
No. 15	S. Shovel	RH	809	1923	2½Cu. Yds.	28ft.	(d)	(4)
5360	E. Stripping Shovel	R&R	1079	1940	8 Cu. Yds.	104ft.	New 3/1940	(5)
24RB	D. Dragline	RB	4951	1940	½Cu. Yd.	60ft.	(e)	(6)

490	E. Shovel. HIgh lift.	R&R	2045	1948	2 Cu. Yds.	36ft.	New 1948	(7)
490	E. Dragline	R&R	2046	1948	1¼ Cu. Yds.	90ft.	New 2/1948	(8)
21RB	D. Shovel	RB	2999	1936	¾ Cu. Yd.	18ft 6ins	(f)	(9)
43RB	D. Dragline	RB	3442	1937	1 Cu. Yd.	60ft.	(g)	(10)
480	E. Shovel	R&R	400	1936			(h)	(11)
54RB	D. Dragline	RB	24553	1960	2 Cu. Yds.	70ft.	(i)	(12)
43RB	D. Shovel	RB	12508	1950	1¾ Cu. Yds.	22ft.	(j)	(13)
54RB	D. Dragline	RB	12509	1951	2 Cu. Yds.	70ft.	(j)	(14)
5W	DE. Walking Dragline	RB	11735	1944	3 Cu. Yds.	135ft.	(k)	(15)
55RB	D. Dragline	RB	5900	1942	2 Cu. Yds.	70ft.	(l)	(16)

(a) ex RH 1924. With grab-35 Cu. ft. 59ft. With 37ft. 6ins jib from 1934
(b) ex Partington Iron & Steel Co Ltd, Wakerley Quarries, per Thos W. Ward Ltd 10/1929
(c) ex Midland Ironstone Co Ltd, Scunthorpe, 5/1930
(d) ex Waltham Iron Ore Co Ltd 1937
(e) ex Waltham Quarries 10/1940; to Waltham 11/1940; ex Waltham 8./1942; to Waltham 8/1942; ex Waltham 4/1953; to Waltham 5/1953. Ex Eastwell Iron Ore Co Ltd 7/1958; to Eastwell 10/1958; ex Eastwell 4/1959.
(f) ex Eastwell Quarries 7/1959; to Eastwell 4/1961; ex Eastwell 10/1961
(g) ex Eastwell Quarries 7/1959; to Eastwell 12/1960; ex Eastwell 10/1961
(h) ex United Steel Cos, Cringle Quarries, 10/1960
(i) ex Mill Hill Quarries c 1961
(j) ex Charwelton Quarries c 3/1962
(k) ex Harlaxton Quarries 10/1964
(l) ex Byfield Quarries 9/1965

(1) At No. 1 quarry. To Lamport Quarries 4/1935; ex Lamport 1/1938. At No. 1 quarry. Scr c 1949
(2) At No,1 quarry. Scr c.1947.
(3) At No. 1 quarry. Scr c 1949
(4) At No. 1 quarry. To Waltham Quarries c 1937
(5) New to No. 1 quarry; to No. 3 quarry 3/1962. Scr 1973
(6) Loading limestone. To Eastwell Quarries 5/1959
(7) New to No. 1 quarry; to No. 3 quarry(?). s/s c 1970
(8) New to No. 1 quarry; to No. 3 quarry. s/s c 1970
(9) To Eastwell Quarries 6/1965
(10) Restoration at No. 1 quarry. s/s c 1966
(11) At No. 1 quarry. s/s
(12) At No. 2 quarry; to Outcrop quarry, 1968 (?). s/s
(13) At No. 2 and/or No. 3 quarry. s/s c 1970
(14) At No. 2 and/or No. 3 quarry. s/s c 1970
(15) At No. 2 quarry; to Outcrop quarry 1968. s/s c 1970
(16) to ?, 8/1966

TILTON QUARRIES

Owners: West Yorkshire Iron & Coal Co Ltd: Stanton Ironworks Co Ltd from 1911; Stewarts & Lloyds Minerals Ltd from 1st January 1950

The ironstone quarries of the Marlstone Rock in Belvoir covered a wide area, continuing eastwards from the Cliff until the gently declining ore bed disappeared under heavier cover or had been eroded away by watercourses. The topography in the neighbourhood of Tilton was very different; "an area of sharp relief" is how Dr D.A. Wray describes it in LI, but the unsuspecting traveller alighting from the train at Tilton station would probably have chosen a coarser term as he laboured up the long steep hill to Halstead, then down and up again to Tilton-on-the-Hill, one and a quarter miles away. The Leicester-Uppingham road is a fair sample, and northwards towards Melton Mowbray the whole area is dotted with hills and dissected by valleys – delightful for the rambler and the archaeologist interested in the sites of deserted villages. Iron is believed to have been smelted in Medieval times near Hallaton, about seven miles to the SSE of Tilton. Ironstone of workable quality is restricted to a few hills and nowhere is there a large area; Tilton is isolated from other ironstone quarries by a minimum of nine miles and it is quite certain that

Tilton Quarries. The thick layer of ironstone revealed in the cutting made by the Joint line south of Tilton station led to its early exploitation. This site is now a nature reserve.
Stanton Ironworks Co Ltd.

it would never have been developed at all but for the G.N.R.-L.N.W.R. Joint line in the dual role of revealing the presence of a rich bed of ironstone in the cutting where Tilton station was built, and providing transport to the ironworks.

The railway between Melton Mowbray and Welham Junction was opened for traffic on 15th December 1879 and the prime mover in negotiations with the Joint Committee to transport the ironstone was William Firth, Chairman of West Yorkshire Iron & Coal Co Ltd, who owned land adjoining the railway at Tilton. From 'Kelly's directory' of 1881 we learn that "ore is obtained at Halstead by Firth and Nelson, who are owners of the land"; and in Leicestershire Record Office is a report, dated December 1880, by Henry Waugh & Co on 'Ironstone on the Berners Estate', which states that the owner of the land adjoining the railway near the station 'is connected with a large ironworks near Leeds', had had samples analysed, and on the results of these tests had opened up ground west of the railway, with an anticipated output of 300 tons per day "when it can be obtained".

The main problem lay in getting the ironstone, outcropping at the top of the bank, down to rail level in the deep cutting, and during the 80 years of operation this was tackled by four entirely separate systems in turn, which is a record as far as ironstone quarry history is concerned. The minutes of the GNR-LNWR Officer's Joint Committee record for 25th June 1880 'Arrangements for working of the incline from the contractor's temporary siding at Tilton were discussed. Mr. Pearce instructed to ask Mr Firth to put in at the foot of the incline safety points leading to a dead end to prevent wagons fouling the traffic siding'; and on 24th September 1880 there were 'prospects of the West Yorkshire Iron & Coal Co Ltd largely increasing the quantity sent from Tilton'. Traffic commenced therefore in 1880; the date of cessation is unknown, but Hewlett quotes 'about 1900' and the siding and connection were taken out on 1st January 1902[1].

There is no definite information on the method of working but the 1890 Railway Clearing House Handbook contains a reference to the 'Tilton Zigzag', and the 1889 OS map shows this feature. These two items, together with the minute of 25th June 1880, indicate a standard gauge zigzag, with three reversals to reach the working face, which was directly west of the station. Operation would presumably be by horses taking one wagon at a time; no locomotive shed is shown on the map, and locomotive operation would have been too cumbrous anyway.

Tilton Quarries. A general view looking west across the Joint Line, of the narrow gauge installation. The tippler is at left centre, with a run of wagons, and the locomotive shed behind them. The quarries were on the high ground to the rear. Traces of earlier ascents of the bank can be noted.
Stanton Ironworks Co Ltd

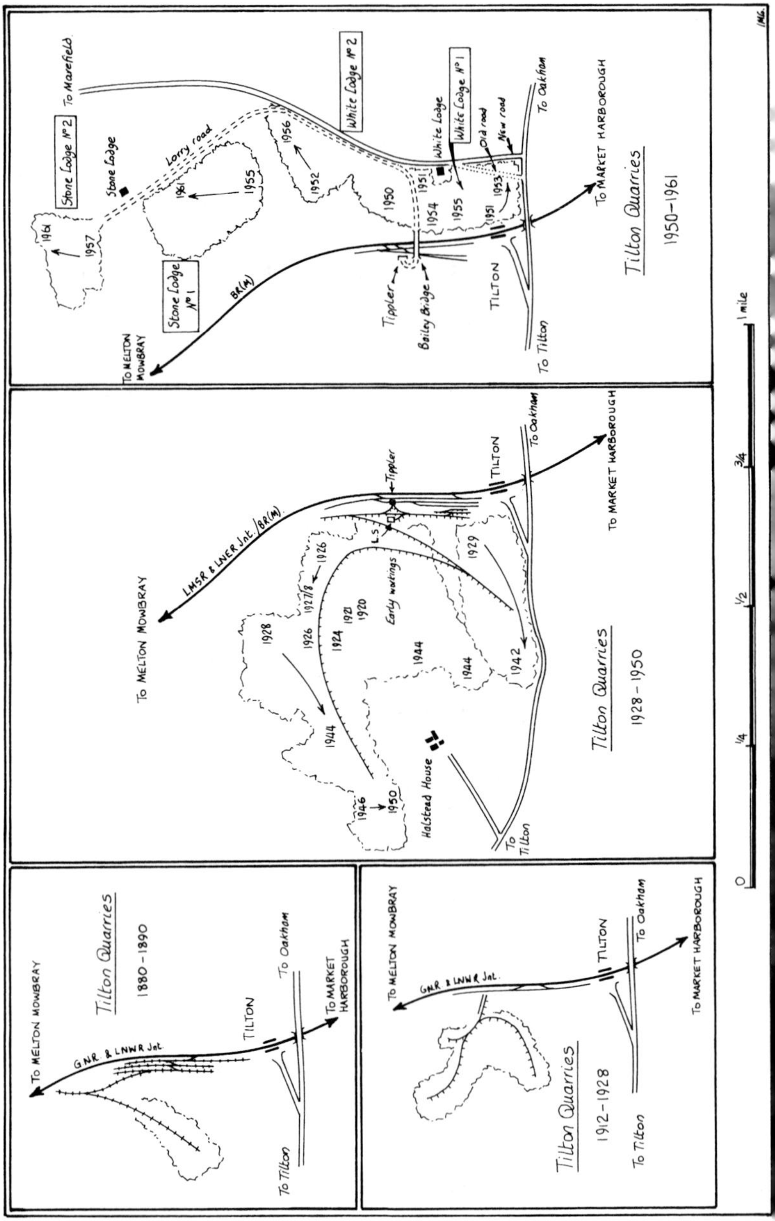
Tilton Quarries
1950-1961
To Marefield
Stone Lodge No 2
Stone Lodge
Lorry road
White Lodge No 2
White Lodge
White Lodge No 1
Old road
New road
To Oakham
To MARKET HARBOROUGH
Stone Lodge No 1
BR(M)
To MELTON MOWBRAY
Tippler
Bailey Bridge
TILTON
To Tilton
Tilton Quarries
1928 - 1950
To MELTON MOWBRAY
LMSR & LNER Jnt./BR(M)
Tippler
L.S.
Early workings
Halstead House
To Tilton
TILTON
To Oakham
To MARKET HARBOROUGH
Tilton Quarries
1880 - 1890
To MELTON MOWBRAY
GNR & LNWR Jnt.
TILTON
To Oakham
To MARKET HARBOROUGH
To Tilton
Tilton Quarries
1912-1928
To MELTON MOWBRAY
GNR & LNWR Jnt.
TILTON
To Oakham
To MARKET HARBOROUGH
To Tilton
0
1/4
1/2
3/4
1 mile

During the twenty years of ownership by the West Yorkshire Iron & Coal Co Ltd, the Tilton quarries had a rather uneven production record, due possibly to vagaries of the trade generally, the distance from the ironworks and the limey character of the ore. After the closure about the turn of the century, the quarries were left standing until 1911, when Stanton Ironworks Co Ltd acquired the lease for the same area; they discovered that admixture with ores from other sources enabled the limey Tilton ore to be used successfully. Stanton introduced an entirely new method of transport in the quarries, with a three-foot gauge tramway running to the head of a cable-worked incline by means of which the end-tipping wooden wagons were lowered to a tipping stage alongside a railway siding north of the station. To do this, the lower part of the incline was built on railway company land, for which permission was sought in January 1912; in October 1912 Stanton also asked the Joint Committee to lower the southern end of the siding and to ease the curve of the northern end to facilitate gravity working. It may be inferred from this that production commenced in 1912. Horses were used for haulage on the quarry tracks. In 1918 Stanton acquired Holwell Iron Co Ltd, and output from Tilton was diverted to Holwell ironworks, where it was mixed with ore from Eaton (Marlstone) and Buckminster (Northampton Sand – more siliceous).

Operations were still small-scale as Stanton worked northwards from the area exhausted by their predecessors; GSM records about 1917 a 900-foot working face. With the postwar drop in demand, the quarries were closed in 1921, but were reopened in 1924. The company purchased the freehold of the remainder of the outcrop and in 1928 the tramway system was remodelled completely to deal with the increased output. The cable-worked incline was replaced by a gravity slope for the tubs; the wooden tipping stage by a rotary tippler; the wooden wagons by squarish steel tubs; and the horses by steam locomotives. The last were essential to work the wagons up and down the bank to the tippler and also to operate a zigzag to the railway siding for bringing up supplies. This zigzag was a more compact affair than the former standard gauge one used by West Yorkshire; the earlier system had four 'steps' at about one in fifty, while the new one ascended the hillside in three steps at about one in twenty-five, and started up from the railway siding area in the opposite direction. It does not seem possible that Stanton could have used much, if any, of the original earthworks, which had in any case been severely altered by the installation of the rope-worked incline.

Tilton Quarries. A 3ft gauge wagon being guided to the tippler frame for emptying. c. 1949
H. Gray

Tilton was the last narrow gauge ironstone line where steam power was introduced, though none of the locomotives concerned were new. BOTTESFORD was the first to arrive, coming from Wartnaby pits that were being closed down. The last arrival, HOLWELL No. 6, came as a replacement for BOTTESFORD, which was by then withdrawn from service, and, standing high in the air at the end of the reversing point on the zigzag, made a perfect photographic shot against the larch plantations on the old quarry workings. The sparse cab of HOLWELL No. 6 would probably not have made her very popular when working on the exposed quarry level in winter, for at 600 feet and more above sea-level, Tilton was the highest ironstone quarry owned by Stewarts & Lloyds Minerals. BOTTESFORD's livery was green lined with black, with red coupling rods and the name painted in black on the tanks. The origin of this name is obscure; in Stanton records the locomotive is referred to as STANTON No. 7, though whether the title was ever carried is uncertain, and it is not quoted in the builder's records. The name itself would be more appropriate to a locomotive working at Woolsthorpe quarries, which were in the estate of the Duke of Rutland, many of whose forebears in the Manners family are buried in Bottesford Church not far away.

Tilton Quarries. All Stanton's 3ft gauge ironstone tramways were delightful to see in action, and Tilton had the extra attraction of being isolated from the rest. A typical Hudswell Clarke, HOLWELL No 6, pauses for the camera on 3rd September 1947.

G. Alliez/courtesy B.D. Stoyel

Tilton Quarries. When and where Bagall 1272 BOTTESFORD received its name is something of a mystery, but she finished up as such and is here shown in derelict condition high up at Tilton on 16th November 1947. L.W. Perkins

There is no record of the locomotive ever having been at Woolsthorpe, but the name alone suggests this as a possibility that has escaped record during the period she is recorded as being at Wartnaby, i.e. before 1929.

STANTON No. 11 had the old Stanton paint style of red-brown lined with yellow (inside) and black (outside), with red rods and the title on cast brass plates on the saddle. The other two locomotives, STANTON No. 9 and HOLWELL No. 6, were green, lined black edged with white, with red rods and brass plates. The locomotive shed was of green-painted corrugated iron and was fitted with lifting tackle in the roof so that boilers could be lifted off frames. Locomotives were exchanged with other quarries according to Stanton's normal policy, but it seems that Tilton was better provided than the other narrow gauge systems, possibly because of its comparative isolation. There was also a separate shed with rail connection for the repair of wagons etc.

In the post-war years only one engine was required in steam, with the other kept as spare; but from 1930 it seems more likely that two locomotives were in use, as two widely (for Tilton, that is!) separated faces were being worked. The northern face was the more important, commencing north-west of the exhausted area, then working anti-clockwise to the south-west, from 1929 up to 1950; the southern face lay between the exhausted area and the Oakham road, working clockwise from near the railway westwards until 1941, by which time the overburden at the Oakham road end had increased to about 15 feet. The overburden at the northern face was still quite shallow at this time. Until the end of 1933, both stone and overburden had been worked by hand, but some blasting to loosen the stone was employed where necessary. In November 1933 a Ruston No. 4 petrol-paraffin dragline was brought in to handle the overburden, presumably at the southern face; this versatile machine, which was small enough to be carried by rail without being dismantled, could be used as a digger, scoop or dragline. Three years later she was replaced by the slightly larger Ransomes & Rapier 431 diesel dragline. From 1942, working was confined to the original northern face and a small westward extension from the earliest quarrying area; the overburden here had now increased, and a Ruston Bucyrus 43RB machine was brought in, and the 431 retained for a few years.

By the end of World War II most of the ironstone outcrop west of the railway had been exhausted, and leases for a similar area east of the railway were obtained. Quarrying on the west ceased in February 1950, and, in accordance with Stanton's policy of doing away with their three-foot gauge systems, the tramway was closed and lifted, and the two remaining locomotives scrapped; Tilton was the last one to go. Transport in the new quarries was entirely by lorries that crossed the railway by a new bridge between the tippler and Tilton station and then released their loads at a brick and concrete tipping chute that was built almost on the site of the rotary tippler, and carried the date 1950 incised in the concrete. From BR's point of view there was no essential change, wagons being released from the upper siding to run under the chute and then into the lower siding for collection when full. Provision of a siding on the other side of the main tracks would have entailed a lot of earth moving in widening a deep cutting at one point and embankment at another, hence the bridge, which was built by Stewarts & Lloyds Minerals Ltd. (though instituted by Stanton) and was of the Bailey Bridge type that had proved so successful in the war. The steel girders were carried on six ferro-concrete piers about 20 feet above rail level, with a bank up to the tipping dock on the west side and to field level on the east, where also the stream was culverted. A concrete road was laid part way across fields, then gravel tracks to the working faces. The locomotive shed was converted to a garage and A.E.C. 'Monarch' lorries used – and possibly other types. The new bridge was officially opened with a small ceremony on 16th March 1950.

Quarrying was more intensive than at the old site; the areas served by the tramway and by the lorry road were approximately equal, but while tramway operation lasted 58 years, the lorries were used only for 11. But in any case the topography hardly allowed any other form of transport. Working commenced in 1950 between the lorry bridge and the Oakham road, extending on three sides of White Lodge, the lane adjacent to which was diverted to permit extraction of the ore beneath; the new junction with the Oakham road was 100 yards to the east. A 43RB crawler diesel dragline was used here. Working at White Lodge No. 1 quarry continued until 1955, by which time operations had already commenced to the north of the lorry bridge; this was White Lodge No. 2 Quarry. The lorry road ran alongside the lane from White Lodge as far as the drive to Stone Lodge, then turned parallel to the drive. This larger area at Stone Lodge was operated by three diesel machines, a 10RB, a 21RB and a 54RB, from 1955 onwards. Production ceased at Stone Lodge No. 1 quarry (south of the drive) in March 1961, and in No. 2 quarry (north of the drive) in July 1961. This was probably as a result of the general contraction in demand for iron ore, as the area was not fully exhausted, and a quarry machine was

Tilton Quarries. Tilton was the last of Stanton's 3ft ironstone lines to give way to lorry transport, and when it did, the ore came from quarries on the opposite side of the BR line, with the lorries using a 'Bailey Bridge' to reach the tipping stage. Collection Eric Tonks

Tilton Quarries. The new tipping dock on the site of the old wagon tippler, with chute for loading wagons. The loco.shed has been modified to house the lorries and extended to provide office accommodation. About 1951. F. Cooper

Tilton Quarries. The Bailey Bridge, looking towards the old quarries, c 1951.
F. Cooper/RRM Archives

Tilton Quarries. Stone Lodge No. 2 quarry, April 1960. 54RB dragline loading the lorry, with a 100RB dragline levelling the spoil heaps. BSC

noted south of the Oakham road in the early 1960s, in possible anticipation of quarrying that side of the road. This however was not done.

The lorries were moved away for work elsewhere and the garage – late loco shed – demolished, though leaving the concrete base with its pit. The BR line did not last much longer either, since Tilton was the main reason for its retention; it was closed on 4th November 1963. The girders of the Bailey Bridge were taken down but the concrete piers left standing, as was the tipping dock. Part of the railway cutting was acquired by the Leicestershire Wildfowlers' Association.

The periods of working at Tilton may be summarised thus:–

West Yorkshire Iron & Coal Co Ltd	1880-1900	West of Rly.	Std. gauge zigzag.	Horse haulage.
Stanton Ironworks Co Ltd.	1912-1928	West of Rly.	3ft. gauge with cable incline.	Horse haulage.
Stanton Ironworks Co Ltd.	1928-1950	West of Rly.	3ft. gauge with rotary tippler.	Steam loco haulage.
Stewarts & Lloyds Minerals Ltd.	1950-1961	East of Rly.	Concrete roads.	Lorry haulage.

Tilton Quarries. The abandoned tipping dock in May 1964. The 1950 date on the stonework can be seen. G. Ordish

The visitor to the site will find many remains to ponder over, but some detection work is necessary to interpret them. From the obvious starting point of the BR trackbed the most prominent feature is the former tipping dock abutment of brick and concrete, still with '1950' clearly visible, and near it are two of the concrete supports of the bridge, one on each side of the railway. From the one on the west side a path climbs the bank and at the top we find the flattened area where the lorries turned, and behind it the concrete foundations of the loco shed, with the pit filled with rubble. Looking north from the back of the shed, the course of the narrow gauge line can be made out, and to the left a low embankment that was probably part of the original standard gauge zigzag. The narrow gauge incline was also situated here but there are no visible traces now, though there were in the 1950s. South (the 'front') of the locomotive shed a fairly wide embankment leads downhill – the later zigzag for the narrow gauge, now overgrown with bushes; its course may be traced (by those equipped with thornproof clothing) down the slope, and at the bottom can be seen the bed of the lower end of the standard gauge gravity siding. Retracing our steps to the locomotive shed, we can discern another tramway course leading upwards south-westerly in a curve; this was the route of Stanton's three-foot tramway to the quarries, and is now hemmed in with trees – but when locomotives were shoving empties up the slope, or holding the full wagons on their descent, the area was much more open. Near the top of the rise the trackbed clears the trees (the plantation here is larch and elder) at a rough stile and then diverges. The left hand fork is a low embankment that peters out after a few yards, but the extent of quarrying can be seen by the remaining face under the hedge parallel with the railway; this was the area worked from 1929 to 1941. The final gullet running up from the Oakham road is still extant, revealing an overburden heavier than the general run at Tilton. The right hand fork runs alongside the hedge and we can make out the position of a reversing junction from which the line went to the main quarrying area. Of the latter virtually no traces remain in the wide fields below Halstead house, but the single-species hedges indicate their one-time presence.

The east side of the railway cutting is planted with conifers, with a concrete 'headstone' incised 'Stanton Plantation 1945', predating quarrying activities on this side – perhaps planted as a windbreak? The concrete road leading up from the bridge is still in position, flanked by ironstone 'benches' in the cutting, but as the road turns parallel with the lane the cutting has been partly filled with farm refuse. Traces of the lorry way can be made out towards Stone Lodge, but the former quarrying area has been smoothed over very thoroughly, leaving only replacement hedges or wire fences as evidence. Even the diverted road route from White Lodge to the Oakham road now has a look of maturity, with its tall hedges (albeit only one species) on each side; behind the western hedge it can be seen that working reached the Oakham road but not beyond it. By peering over the railway bridge on the south side, the deep cutting that revealed the presence of ironstone at Tilton can still be seen, but it is now very heavily overgrown: it is now a nature reserve in the care of the Leicestershire & Rutland Trust for Nature Conservation.

Because of its limited area, Tilton was never an important quarry, but its very isolation gave it an added charm. In this part of Leicestershire, all hills and valleys, there are plenty of lanes but few people, no less than six villages depopulated by enclosure or plague lying within a short distance. One was on the top of Whatborough Hill, at 755 feet one of the highest points in the county, and overlooking the Tilton quarries. Then there is Robin-a-Tiptoe Hill – delightful sounding name belied by its origin; for here was hanged the highwayman Robin, whose toes just brushed the grass. The naturalist finds much to interest him, and so too the social historian; at one time the industrial railway enthusiast could find picturesque narrow gauge locomotives decorating the upland scene. Alas, they are no more, and only the industrial archaeologist can discover where they ran.

Footnote

1. Minutes of GNR-LNWR Officer's Joint Committee. I am indebted to Geoffrey Webb for extracting these.

Grid References

760060	Tipping dock/tippler; foot of zig-zag
759061	Top of incline
760061	Locomotive shed
751061	Terminus of north face, Halstead House
754056	Terminus by main road
761060	Bailey Bridge
760070	Terminus of quarry road, north end
764065	Terminus of quarry road, south end
763057	Diversion of road, north end
765065	End of road

Locomotives

Gauge: 3ft 0ins

BOTTESFORD	0-6-0T	OC WB 1272	1180	9 x 13½ins	2ft 2ins	(a)	Scr 12/1948
STANTON No. 11	0-6-0ST	OC HC 277	1885	9 x 15ins	2ft 6ins	(b)	Scr 1/1950
STANTON No. 9	0-4-0ST	OC HC 506	1898	9 x 15ins	2ft 3ins	(c)	(1)
(f. DENTON)		Reb. Wake	1916				
HOLWELL No. 6	0-4-0ST	OC HC 375	1890	10 x 16ins	2ft 9ins	(d)	Scr 7/1950
		Reb. 1/1913					

(a) ex Holwell Works., 3/1929 (prev. at Wartnaby Quarries)
(b) ex Woolsthorpe Quarries 2/1930
(c) ex Woolsthorpe Quarries 7/1937
(d) ex Eaton Quarries 1/1946

(1) to Eaton Ropeway 4/1941

Quarry Machines

No. 4	PP. Dragline	RH 1200	1927	⅜ Cu. Yd.	40ft.	(a)	(1)
431	D. Dragline	R&R 431	1936	½ Cu. Yd.	50ft.	New c 6/1936	(2)
43RB	D. Dragline. Long Jib. Crawler	RB 3856	1938	¾ Cu. Yd.	70ft.	(b)	(3)
21RB	D. Dragline	RB 2511	1934	¾ Cu. Yd.	40ft.	(c)	(4)
21RB	D. Dragline	RB 3306	1937	⅜ Cu. Yd.	50ft.	(d)	(5)
10RB	D. Clamshell Excavator	RB 14897	1952		35ft.	(e)	(6)
54RB	D. Dragline	RB 22355	1957			New 12/1957	(7)

(a) ex South Witham Quarries 11/1933
(b) ex Eaton Quarries 4/1941
(c) ex South Witham Quarries 3/1943
(d) ex Eaton Quarries 6/1952
(e) ex Wirksworth Quarries, Derbyshire, by 1958.

(1) At Tilton quarry. To Nuthall sandpits, Nottinghamshire 9/1936; ex Nuthall 1/1945. At Tilton quarry. To Glendon Quarries 11/1945
(2) New to Tilton quarry. To Buckminster Quarries 7/1940; ex Buckminster 7/1946. At Tilton quarry. To Woolsthorpe Quarries 6/1951.
(3) At Tilton quarry; to White Lodge quarries by 1952. To Stanton ironworks 3/1958
(4) At Tilton quarry. To Holwell Quarries 6/1943
(5) At Stone Lodge quarries. To F. Cowman Ltd., dealer 2/1962
(6) At Stone Lodge quarries. To Crane Engineering Ltd, Ketley, Salop, 10/1964
(7) New to Stone Lodge quarries. To Market Overton Quarries c 1963

NEVILL HOLT QUARRIES
Owners: W.J. Roseby; B. Thornton from 1862: Medbourne Bridge Iron Ore Co from 1871.

The isolated outcrop of stone on the hilltop at Nevill Holt was one of the earliest in Leicestershire to be worked, but never achieved any great influence; there was quite a lot of history attached to it, in fact, but little production. The workings were opened up in 1861 under the supervision of Mr W.J. Roseby, who disposed of his interests to Mr B. Thornton and moved to Lincolnshire to take up a position as manager and mineral agent for Roland Winn (Frodingham Ironstone Mines). The new owner had ambitious plans including the erection of blast furnaces and rolling mills – a surprising decision in view of the demonstrably limited ore reserves of the outcrop – and the foundations of four furnaces were laid, but owing to financial difficulties the work was abandoned[1,2] and quarrying seems to have ceased in 1868. Staveley Coal & Iron Co Ltd expressed an interest but nothing transpired. How the iron ore was transported from the quarry, and where it went, are not known. The later operator used a cable-worked incline to bring the wagons down, but this was apparently not constructed until 1873. So, if the previous owners used an inclined tramway, it must have been lifted after closure; more likely however horse and cart were used, as the output could only have been very small.

In 1871 there were two schemes for revival. The Leicestershire Ironstone & Smelting Co Ltd was promulgated with the object of purchasing about 1,000 acres of land 'in the parishes of Holt, Medbourne and Bradley (?Ashley)' to work ironstone and erect blast furnaces[3]; nothing came of this but the other scheme had more success, as the Medbourne Bridge Iron Ore Co[2], under the aegis of J. Roseby (son of W.J. Roseby). The company title implies that they had decided simply to sell the ore and had abandoned any idea of putting up furnaces on the site. It was therefore necessary to transport the ore to the railway and for this purpose a self-acting double track incline was built from t he quarry at the summit (450 foot O.D.) to the foot of the hill (200 feet O.D.) where the ore was transferred to standard gauge wagons on a short branch from the LNWR Market Harborough-Peterborough line; this branch crossed the River Welland and then passed beneath the Drayton-Medbourne road by a substantial brick bridge. The total distance from quarry to main line was two-thirds of a mile and of the standard gauge section only 50 yards

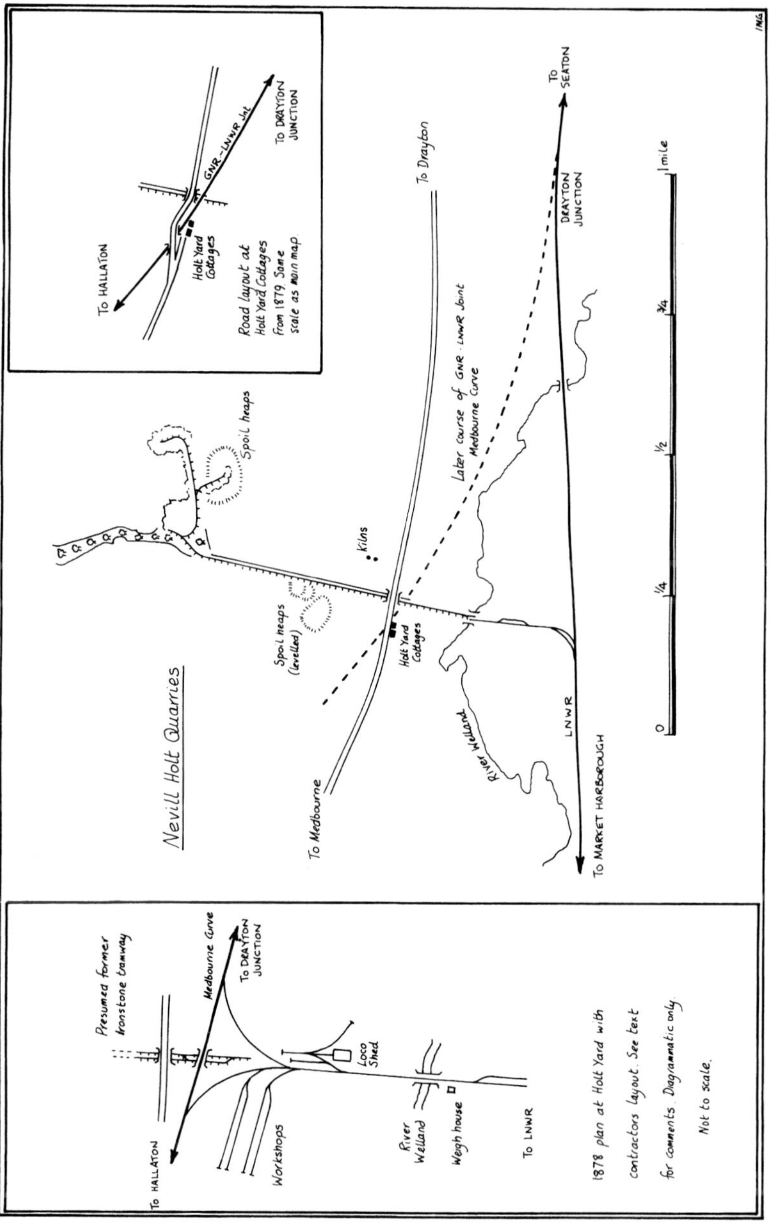
Nevill Holt Quarries
Spoil heaps
Spoil heaps (levelled)
Kilns
Holt Yard Cottages
To Medbourne
To Drayton
Later course of GNR · LNWR Joint Medbourne Curve
River Welland
LNWR
To MARKET HARBOROUGH
DRAYTON JUNCTION
TO SEATON
0
1/4
1/2
3/4
1 mile
TO HALLATON
GNR - LNWR Jnt
TO DRAYTON JUNCTION
Holt Yard Cottages
Road layout at Holt Yard Cottages From 1879. Same scale as main map
Presumed former ironstone tramway
Medbourne Curve
To DRAYTON JUNCTION
To HALLATON
Workshops
Loco Shed
River Welland
Weigh house
To LNWR
1878 plan at Holt Yard with contractors layout. See text for comments. Diagrammatic only.
Not to scale.
IMG

belonged to the LNWR. The portion south of the Welland was in Northamptonshire, all the rest in Leicestershire.

The incline was tried for the first time in the last week of May 1873 and was marred by a frightful accident in which the foreman, John Neal, was seriously injured and who died very shortly afterwards. At the inquest, reported in the 'Northampton Mercury' of 7th June 1873, Neal was said to have had sole control in the construction and had latterly supervised the building of the incline, which was on the common funicular principle, with descending wagons hauling up empties, but under the control of a brakesman at the summit. The cable was carried on steel rollers between the rails.

Poor John Neal died in vain; the Medbourne Bridge Iron Ore Co lasted only until 1874. Rails and other equipment were advertised for sale in 'Iron' for 13th November 1875, p.624; the company was then stated to be in liquidation. A portion of the site was obliterated in 1879 by the cutting of the LNWR-GNR Medbourne Curve between the Peterborough and Melton Mowbray lines, and Holt Yard on the south side of the road was used as a depot for the gangs employed on the work. A book of fine coloured drawings of buildings and contractor's equipment, dated 1878 and kept in the Leicestershire Record Office, contains a detailed layout of Holt Yard; this includes the tracks under the road bridge that had presumably been left in by the ironstone operators, since they served no purpose for the current work, and indeed appear to have been partly lifted to accommodate connections to the new railway line. On one of the severed lines is marked 'engine shed', on the north bank of the river, adjacent to the bridge; but if this was used by the ironstone operators, we have no record of the locomotive it held. The 1884 OS shows the standard gauge section terminating at a point just south of the Welland, the lines in Holt Yard evidently having been lifted when the contractors had finished. In trying to decipher the evidence on the ground, it must be remembered that the 1878 operations may well have modified matters.

The history of ownership is thus fairly well documented and even today, more than a century since ironstone quarrying ceased, there are remains enough to indicate the general layout and method of operation; no personal recollections appear to have survived, as it is rather an isolated spot from which employees dispersed on closure. The tramway seems to have been of about 2ft 6ins gauge and of double track up the hillside, for working on the common funicular principle; in the quarry beyond the winding drum the tubs would probably be pushed by hand, or possibly hauled by pony. The point of transhipment to standard gauge is open to doubt and is now probably beyond resolution. The 1884 O.S. shows the standard gauge siding terminating at a point just south of the Welland (the narrow gauge having been lifted by then) which suggests that transhipment was here rather than the more obvious place at the foot of the incline; this could well have been done to save money on the bridge over the river. Of the standard gauge section only 50 yards belonged to the LNWR,[4] the rest presumably to the ironstone operators, who probably used a horse to work it. The bridge itself was out of strict alignment with the embankments, particularly the northern one; there was a retaining wall along the river bank for the width of the embankment, with the bridge only extending to half way, on the west side. On the south bank the retaining wall just accommodated the bridge but the embankment went a little further east. There were some wooden piles in the river east of the bridge suggesting possible provision for a wider structure. The bridge consisted of sleepers carried by three main steel girders, while the abutment walls were of red brick with tetrahedral tops of blue brick to the end pillars. The rails of the bridge consisted of a pair of rather flimsy-looking wooden rails, and the whole structure suggestive of narrow gauge operation. South of the river the line to the LNWR was carried on a low embankment composed of ironstone rubble and pierced by several stone arches presumably for flood relief. There was no indication of a raised tipping dock, so transhipment was probably by sideways shovelling.

The river bridge was very decrepit in 1950, and in 1968 Peter Staughton reported that most of the wooden decking had gone, the rest mostly rotten, and some of the wooden side rails missing; the brickwork and masonry was also in a very poor state. It was demolished shortly afterwards and replaced by a modern concrete structure with a gate at each end; a portion of the trackbed beyond had been cleared and used as an apiary. North of the bridge the site of the locomotive shed can be made out and traces of former sidings towards the road bridge; the latter is intact, with two arches clear on the north side but – as seems inevitable – choked with rubbish on the south. The trackbed in the cutting north of this bridge is waterlogged but the incline itself is clearly defined and intact apart from where a new barn has been built across the formation, which is paralleled above this point on the east side by a new wooden fence. On the west side of the incline is a substantial spoil heap, the top of which is levelled off. At the top of the incline the course of the line passes into the

Nevill Holt Quarries. View up the incline of the former tramway, from the road bridge. The quarries were among the trees at the top of the hill. 7th April 1954. G.H. Starmer

Nevill Holt Quarries. Tramway bridge over the river Welland. This decrepit structure has now been replaced by a modern concrete bridge. P. Staughton

workings, clothed with trees; a fence is at the entrance and from it one can gaze down and pick out the route, clearly defined all the way to the now-vanished BR line.

The quarry remains are very clear, with the tramway turning eastwards from the summit in a cutting through limestone rock. On the north side is a roughly square quarry, again seemingly for limestone, and the tramway route continues for a further 300 yards and then turns north. The west-east section is bordered on the south side by an embankment, pierced at one point, through which gap a branch tramway led east-south-east to the ironstone face. Working appears to have taken place from the outcrop northwards and the dumped overburden, instead of filling in a worked-out area in the usual way, was spread down the hillside. These hummocks of mainly limestone 'rubbly' are covered in late summer with the grass known as 'Yorkshire Fog' and hundreds of plants of the handsome Nodding Thistle; the contrast with the dark green grass of the original fields is very striking indeed. Half way up the hillside, and 50 yards east of the incline there used to be some brickworks unconnected with the tramway; their weed-encrusted ruins, whose isolation made them quite impressive, were demolished in the 1960s.

Half a mile to the north of the quarries just described, a quarry for agricultural lime was opened by C.A.E.C. Howard Ltd in October 1942[5], using road transport; by an odd coincidence the same company operated a similar limestone quarry at Leadenham, between Lincoln and Grantham, and which also succeeded earlier efforts to extract ironstone lower down the hillside. Nevill Holt, as an isolated outcrop of Lincolnshire Limestone, is of considerable interest to geologists, and the abundant traces of ironstone operations from the overgrown quarries down to the former railway junction merit the attention of the industrial archaeologist.

Footnotes

1. J.W. Judd: Geology of Rutland and parts of Northamptonshire: Geological Survey Memoirs, 1874, p.112.
2. Mining Journal, 19th June 1868, p.670; and 29th July 1871, p.652.
3. The Engineer, 24th November 1871.
4. Thanks to Mr C. R. Clinker for this information.
5. The Lincolnshire Limestone of Nevill Holt, Leicestershire; Anthony Hallam. Reprinted 1954 from the Transactions of the Leicester Literary and Philosophical Society, XLVIII.

Grid References

811916	Junction with LNWR
812918	Bridge over Welland
812921	Bridge under road
813926	Top of incline
815932	Limestone Quarry (centre)
816927	Gullet terminus
817924	Terminus of branch to dump rubble

EXPLANATION OF TABLES

Locomotives

The columns show in order:– title: type: cylinder position: maker: maker's number: year built: cylinder dimensions: driving wheel diameter: origin: disposal. In referring to these columns the following points should be noted.

Title. Unofficial names used by the staff but not carried by the engine are denoted by inverted commas.
Type. The Whyte system of wheel classification is used, but if wheels are not connected by outside rods they are shown as 4w, 6w as the case may be.The following abbreviations are used:

T	Side Tank	DM	Diesel Mechanical	BE	Battery Electric
PT	Pannier Tank	DE	Diesel Electric	WE	Wire Electric
ST	Saddle Tank	DH	Diesel Hydraulic		
WT	Well Tank	PM	Petrol Mechanical		
VB	Vertical Boiler	PE	Petrol Electric		
G	Geared	PMR	Petrol Mechanical Railcar		

Cylinder Position	IC	Inside Cylinders
	OC	Outside Cylinders
	VC	Vertical Cylinders

Makers. The following abbreviations are used, with lesser known builders' names being given in full:

AB	Andrew Barclay Sons & Co Ltd, Kilmarnock
AE	Avonside Engine Co Ltd, Bristol
AP	Aveling & Porter Ltd, Rochester
B	Barclays & Co, Kilmarnock
BEV	British Electric Vehicles Ltd. Southport
Bg	E E. Baguley Ltd, Burton on Trent
BH	Black Hawthorn & Co Ltd. Gateshead
Bton	Brighton Locomotive Works, LB&SCR
CF	Chapman & Furneaux Ltd, Gateshead
DC	Drewry Car Co Ltd, London (Suppliers only)
DK	Dick, Kerr & Co Ltd, Preston
EE	English Electric Co Ltd, Preston
EV	Ebbw Vale Steel Coal & Iron Co Ltd, Ebbw Vale
FE	Falcon Engine & Car Works Ltd, Loughborough
FH	F. C. Hibberd & Co Ltd, London
FW	Fox Walker & Co Bristol
GB	Greenwood & Batley Ltd, Leeds
GEC/USA	General Electric Co, USA

H	James & Frederick Howard Ltd, Bedford
HC	Hudswell Clarke & Co Ltd, Leeds
HCR	Hudswell Clarke & Rodgers. Leeds
HE	Hunslet Engine Co Ltd, Leeds
HL	Hawthorn Leslie & Co Ltd, Newcastle upon Tyne
Hu	Robert Hudson Ltd, Leeds
JF	John Fowler & Co (Leeds) Ltd
K	Kitson & Co Ltd, Leeds
KE	Kilmarnock Engineering Co Ltd
KS	Kerr, Stuart & Co Ltd, Stoke on Trent
Mkm	Markham & Co Ltd, Chesterfield
MR	Motor Rail Ltd, Bedford
MW	Manning Wardle & Co Ltd, Leeds
N	Neilson & Co, Glasgow
OK	Orenstein & Koppel AG, Berlin
P	Peckett & Sons Ltd, Bristol
RH	Ruston & Hornsby Ltd, Lincoln
RR	Rolls Royce Ltd, Shrewsbury
RS	Robert Stephenson & Co Ltd, Newcastle upon Tyne and Darlington
RSH	Robert Stephenson & Hawthorns Ltd, Newcastle upon Tyne
S	Sentinel (Shrewsbury) Ltd
Sdn	Swindon Locomotive Works, GWR
SS	Sharp Stewart & Co Ltd, Glasgow
VF	Vulcan Foundry Ltd. Newton-le-Willows
WB	W. G. Bagnall Ltd, Stafford
YE	Yorkshire Engine Co Ltd, Sheffield

Maker's Number. Reb = Rebuilt.

Year Built. The year quoted is that given on the maker's plate, or from the maker's records if the date does not appear on the plate.

Cylinder and Driving Wheel Dimensions. These apply to locomotive as new.

Origin. 'New' indicates that the locomotive was delivered by the makers to this location at the stated date (to the month where known). Transfers from elsewhere are indicated by a bracketed letter and appropriate footnote.

Disposal.. Locomotives transferred to another owner or site are shown by a bracketed number with corresponding footnote. Scr = Scrapped. s/s = scrapped or sold, disposal unknown.

Quarry Machines

The information is set out in much the same way as for locomotives, but as collected information on quarry machines has not appeared before we give rather more in the way of explanation. The columns show in order:- title (if any): class description: power source and type of machine: maker: maker's number: year built: bucket capacity: jib or boom length: origin: disposal.

Title. Often machines carried no title. but major operators such as Stewarts & Lloyds Minerals Ltd gave them numbers, quoted where known; and a very few were named.

Class Description. Steam machines were most commonly referred to as '10-ton', '20-ton', etc, the 'ton' referring not to the weight but to the cutting pressure on the bucket teeth. Ruston Proctor & Co Ltd adopted these as class numbers, a No. 20 machine being a '20-ton' and so on, and these class numbers have been used in the tables, as in the manufacturer's literature. Whitaker's used a letter code but unfortunately only in a few cases do we know these. so we have had to fall back on '12-ton' etc. Ruston & Hornsby Ltd used designatory numbers for larger machines, e.g. No. 250.

Diesel and electric machines were given class numbers by Ruston Bucyrus Ltd from a scheme used by the Bucyrus Co. The early machines were described as 37B, 43B etc but this was later changed to 37RB and 43RB etc, and we have used the latter throughout lor simplicity. The numbers correspond roughly with the wieight of the machine in tons. Ransomes & Rapier Ltd applied class numbers such as 422, 480 etc, and also used these numbers for steam machines of the same power. The large Walking Draglines of both manufacturers incorporated 'W' in the class description – 3W, 5W for RB in ascending order of size, and W 150, W 1400 etc for R&R, the numbers again corresponding roughly to the weights.

Power Source and Type of Machine. The power source is indicated by a letter: S – Steam: D – Diesel. DE – Diesel Electric: E – Electric. PP – Petrol-paraffin.

The two main types of machine are shovels and draglines. In simple terms, the latter were used primarily tor removing overburden by dragging the bucket up the working face by a chain in a scraping motion, then slewing the bucket round to dump the load on the worked-out area; a shovel would then dig out the ore beneath. Obviously there are many variants on these according to circumstances, and digger drivers were very adept in using their machines in difficult positions. Some removal of overburden was done by 'stripping shovels' of large size. The form and duties of various specialized machines will be obvious from their names – crane. clamshell. back-acter, etc. Some machines were rail-mounted, some on crawlers or 'Caterpillar' tracks. When the type of machine is uncertain. the term 'navvy' is used.

Makers. The following abbreviations are used, with lesser known builder's narnes being given in full.

At	Atlantic Equipment Co, USA
BE	Bucyrus-Erie Co, USA
Berry	Henry Berry & Co Ltd, Leeds
Bu	Bucyrus Co, USA
Lima	Baldwin Lima Hamilton Co, USA
Marion	Marion Steam Shovel Co, USA
NBM	Newton, Bean & Mitchell, Bradford
Priestman	Priestman Brothers Ltd, Hull
RB	Ruston Bucyrus Ltd, Lincoln

RH	Ruston &: Hornsby Ltd, Lincoln
RP	Ruston Proctor & Co Ltd, Lincoln
R&R	Ransomes & Rapier Ltd, Ipswich
S&P	Stothert & Pitt Ltd, Bath
Taylor Hubbard	Taylor Hubbard & Co Ltd, Leicester
Wh	Whitaker Bros Ltd, Leeds
Wilson	John H. Wilson & Co Ltd, Liverpool

Makers' Number and **Year Built.** These are taken from manufacturers' records in the case of the Ruston companies and from R & R; from operators' records otherwise.

Bucket Capacity and **Jib or Boom Length.** The figures come from operators' records mostly, sometimes from manufacturers. There is no hard and fast rule about the terms 'jib' and 'boom' but generally steam machines are spoken of as having jibs, and diesel and electric machines booms, particularly the larger machines.

Origin. 'New' means that the machine was supplied by the makers to this location. The months quoted are those shown as delivery dates in the makers' records; but very often machines were supplied in sections to be assembled on site (this being particularly so with large machines) so that some time elapsed before they entered service. Transfers from other locations are shown by bracketed letters and appropriate footnotes. To save space, these footnotes also include details of any changes in bucket capacity or jib length.

Disposal. A machine transferred to another location is shown by a bracketed number and corresponding footnote Scr = scrapped- s/s = scrapped or sold, disposal unknown. These footnotes also include known details of the individual quarries or working faces that the machine served in the system concerned, with dates where known

Sources of Information. The principal sources of information consulted and quoted from, using the abbreviations given, are as follows. All were published by Her/His Majesty's Stationery Office.

Mineral Statistics of Great Britain. Robert Hunt	1853–81	(MS)
Mineral Statistics of Great Britain. Geological Survey Memoirs	1882–94	(MS)
List of Quarries in the United Kingdom and the Isle of Man	1895–1934	(LQ)
Special Reports on the Mineral Resources of Great Britain: Part XII – Iron Ore. Geological Survey Memoirs	1920	(GSM)
The Mesozoic Ironstone of England: The Northampton Sand Ironstone	1951	(NSI)
The Mesozoic Ironstone of England: The Liassic Ironstones	1952	(LI)

INDEX